We have _____
week on Tuesdays.

P. E. Rouse,
Central College,
Fayette,
Mo,
February 26, 1907.

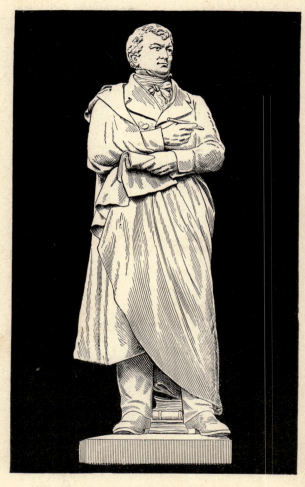

STATUE OF HEINRICH ZSCHOKKE, BY LANZ,
AARAU, 1895.

Der zerbrochene Krug

Novelle

von

Heinrich Zschokke

EDITED WITH INTRODUCTION, NOTES AND
VOCABULARY, AND
PARAPHRASES FOR RETRANSLATION INTO GERMAN

BY

EDWARD S. JOYNES

PROFESSOR OF MODERN LANGUAGES IN SOUTH CAROLINA COLLEGE

BOSTON, U.S.A.

D. C. HEATH & CO., PUBLISHERS

1906

COPYRIGHT, 1898
BY EDWARD S. JOYNES

PRINTED IN
UNITED STATES
OF AMERICA

PREFACE.

THE following charming and simple story is edited expressly for early and easy reading. In recent years a great number of excellent texts have been added to our resources in German; but of those especially adapted, in style and editorial treatment, for very easy reading the list is still quite limited. To that list the present edition is intended to belong. The text is very simple, both in matter and in style. The Notes aim to give such help as young students — not quite beginners — should need. The Vocabulary is adapted to the same grade, presuming a knowledge of only the simplest and most regular grammatical forms. The Paraphrases for retranslation are, like the text, simple and easy; yet the teacher — still more the student — will not fail to see that they include many suggestive turns of phrase and construction. Purposely, for convenience of selection or of review, these exercises are divided under each section into two parts. The mode of using them — or whether to use them at all — will, of course, be determined by teachers themselves.

Different editions of this text show occasional, and sometimes considerable, differences of reading. The copy here followed is — with very slight variation — that of the latest edition in Cotta's *Volksbibliothek.*

SOUTH CAROLINA COLLEGE,
NOVEMBER, 1897.

PREFACE.

THE following charming and simple story is edited expressly for easy and easy reading. In recent years a great
number of excellent texts have been added to our resources
in German; but of these, especially adapted in style and
editorial treatment for very easy reading, the list is still
quite limited. To that list the present edition is intended
to belong. The text is very simple, both in matter and in
style. The point aimed to give such help as young students
of reading beginners—should need. The Vocabulary is
adapted to the same grade, containing a knowledge of only
the simplest and most regular grammatical forms. The
Biographies for translation are, like the text simple and
easy. And the teacher—will trust the student—will not
find it so that they in little more suggestive form of phrases
and construction. Exercises for convenient of selection
or of review, these exercises are divided under each section
in two parts. The mode of using them—any scheme to
use them at all—with, of course, be determined by teachers
themselves.

Different editions of this text show occasional and sometimes considerable differences of reading. The copy here
followed is—with very slight variations—that of the latest
edition in Gerth's Text-Sammlung.

NORTH CAROLINA COLLEGE,
NOVEMBER, 1897.

INTRODUCTION.

THE life of Zschokke was one of remarkably varied activity and achievment. Besides his very considerable literary work he was laborious and conspicuous as educator, as editor, as statesman, patriot and philanthropist. He combined large idealism and spirituality with practical judgment and great energy of character. His long life was devoted earnestly and unselfishly to the good of mankind; and his name, though not of the most illustrious, is highly and widely honored in Switzerland and in Germany. Such a biography is of unique interest, but here only a very brief sketch will be presented.

JOHANN HEINRICH DANIEL ZSCHOKKE was born at Magdeburg in Prussia, March 22, 1771, of intelligent and well-to-do parents of the middle class. Early an orphan, he passed an ill-directed, misunderstood, unhappy and somewhat wayward childhood. His early education was irregular, and his backwardness in study led to the belief — shared also by himself — that he was unfitted for intellectual life. Yet he was busy with other thoughts — especially with unwholesome introspection and religious doubts, and a vague longing for liberty and for sympathy. Finally, in his seventeenth year, he ran away from school, to seek liberty at any cost. For two years he led a wandering and precarious life, now teaching privately, for which he was ill prepared, now trying his pen in the service of a company of actors — living poorly and hardly, yet reading eagerly as he had opportunity, and gaining meanwhile valuable insight into life, and into himself. These roving years, which might have wrecked a less sturdy character, were of great service to Zschokke. They gave him needed experience; they cured him of morbid introspection and doubt; they fired him with ambition to be and to do something better, and convinced him of the need of education, discipline and self-reliance.

Accordingly at the end of two years he returned home, sought reconciliation with his guardian, and in 1790 matriculated in the University at Frankfurt on the Oder as a student of theology. At the same time he extended his course of study over a wide range of philosophy, history, politics and natural science, and was truly an omnivorous and voracious student. In 1792 he took his doctor's degree with distinction and passed his examination in theology; yet, being deemed too young for the pulpit, he continued at the university as *Privat Docent.* Here, besides theology, he lectured on ethics, æsthetics, history and sociology; he also found time to produce an extravagant play, *Abellino, der grosse Bandit* — somewhat in the style of Schiller's *Robbers* — of which he afterward heartily repented, yet which was long popular on the stage; and soon after, another, of less distinction, *Julius von Sassen.* His lectures were very successful, and it seemed that a career of distinction as university professor was open before him. But these were the days of the French revolution, and Zschokke, early inspired with zeal for liberty, had made known only too clearly his sympathy with this great movement for human rights. His application in 1795 for promotion to a professorship was rudely rejected by the Prussian minister. Convinced that there was no self-respecting career for him either at the university or within the Prussian dominions, he surrendered his position, and started out again — no longer a callow youth but a cultured and thoughtful man — to seek his fortune.

He went first to Switzerland, where he hoped to find a primitive people in the enjoyment of their natural rights ; but, while he was delighted with the natural features of the country, he was astonished and shocked at the political and social condition of the people. Still he prolonged his visit, making many valued and valuable friends. He next went to Paris (1796), where, at the very source of the revolution, he hoped to see in reality his ideal of political liberty. But he was soon disenchanted and, disappointed and aimless, he turned away to resume his travels — this time through Switzerland to Rome. Detained by accident at Chur, he was induced to take charge of an academy at Reichenau, formerly a flourishing and influential school, now however in decadence. This invitation offered Zschokke an opportunity to put into practice his ideas on education. He soon reformed and transformed the school, founding its organization especially upon the ideas of liberty, self-government and training for free citizenship. In two years he had brought his work to a condition of great usefulness and promise. But by this time France and Austria were again at war. Switzerland, the common frontier, was the battleground, and the prey of both. The inhabitants were now divided into contending parties. The school was closed, and as the Austrian influence was here in the ascendant, Zschokke became a fugitive, again disappointed of his most cherished hopes. Meantime, however, he had established a high reputation as an educator and had gained standing and influence among prominent men of the liberal party. He had already produced, besides a valuable schoolbook, an interesting work on local history, and his labors had met with public recognition by his formal admission to the rights of honorary citizenship.

At Ragatz Zschokke met other refugees, like himself friendly to the popular cause. By them he was appointed delegate to the Helvetic government then sitting at Aarau. This (Aug., 1798) marks his entrance into public life. For the stormy years following it is impossible, and here needless, to recount his history. Winning applause and confidence on his first public appearance, he was appointed successively to office after office of responsibility, trial and peril. Everywhere he acted as the champion of the rights of the people, as peacemaker between contending factions, as the protector of communities and of persons under the horrors of war. In every capacity his clear judgment, his patriotic faith, his high courage and generous heart were manifest and won for him the respect of foes and the admiration of friends; so that it is hardly too much to say that during these trying years he was among the foremost citizens of his adopted country. On the restoration of peace Zschokke occupied high official position; but as he was not in sympathy with the reactionary tendencies of the government, he withdrew from public life — yet spent another quiet and fruitful winter (1801-2) at Berne.

Withdrawn now, as he supposed permanently, from public affairs, yet unwilling to leave Switzerland, he settled (1802) at Aarau, where he ultimately built for himself a charming home. Here, in 1805, he married happily and founded a large family. After the more liberal reforms introduced by Napoleon, he once more took part in the public affairs of the canton, and was the leading spirit in all movements, official or private, for the general welfare, and especially in behalf of education, and the improvement of the domestic condition, the morals and the taste of the people. But chiefly now he employed himself in literary work. Here he lived to the close of his long life (June 27, 1848) in indefatigable activity as citizen and as author, revered in Switzerland and highly honored abroad for his public services, and winning wide fame and influence by his pen. The lapse of time, in a generation no longer attracted by his admirable personal character and distinguished career, has somewhat obscured his literary reputation; but in Switzerland his name is still honored among the protagonists of the national liberty, and his more popular writings are still quite widely read in Germany also. On the 13th of July 1895, by general contribution, a superb bronze statue — the work of the sculptor Alfred Lanz — was erected to his memory at Aarau.

Zschokke's extensive literary work — the entire collection includes forty volumes — covers a wide range of topics and of style, and reveals his varied powers and many-sided character, as well as his limitations. Though not attaining the highest rank in any field, he was excellent in all; and such was his knowledge of and sympathy with our common humanity, that his works have had wider reading and influence than many others of far higher and more permanent literary rank. Outside of his early dramas, *Abellino* and

Julius (mentioned above) whose youthful extravagance he himself wished forgotten, we may mention in the field of history — besides numerous shorter sketches of more local interest — his important *Geschichte des bayerischen Volks und seiner Fürsten*, and especially *Des Schweizerlandes Geschichte für das Schweizer Volk*. This was written in a familiar and charming style, expressly to reach the common people and to arouse national pride and patriotism. It was Zschokke's motto: *Volksbildung ist Volksbefreiung;* he held that the reverent study of a nation's history is an important part of the patriotic education of its citizens, and to that object this work — even yet a household book in Switzerland — has powerfully contributed.

Of Zschokke's numerous works of fiction many were written with the like object, the education or improvement of the people. Such "novels with a purpose" are usually dry reading; but many of Zschokke's are redeemed by keen insight of character, a lively style and often a playful humor. We may name *Das Goldmacherdorf, Alamontade, der Galeerensklave, Meister Jordan, Die Branntweinpest.* Besides these there is a long list of others, sometimes with historical background, as *Addrich im Moos, Die Rose von Disentis,* etc.; others purely fictitious, often humorous, yet sometimes with deeper meaning; such as: *Das Abenteuer einer Neujahrsnacht, Hans Dampf in allen Gassen, Herrn Quints Verlobung, Das Wirtshaus zu Cransac,* etc. In all his fiction, of whatever character, Zschokke's plots and portraits are always pure. Nothing unclean soils his pages. His treatment of woman and of love is always delicate and tender.

In addition to these numerous books Zschokke's labors

as an editor were large and various. From 1799, and then
after an interval from 1804 to 1842, he conducted a weekly
paper, *Der aufrichtige und wohlerfahrne Schweizerbote*,
which was widely read, and added much to his reputation
at that day. To this he added later an annual *Kalender
des Schweizerboten*, including original work as well as laborious compilations. He issued also, for several years, a
periodical of useful knowledge : *Miscellen für die neueste
Weltkunde*, and later a historical Magazine, *Zur Geschichte
unserer Zeit*, and in addition to these, still later, *Erheite-
rungen*, a magazine of lighter literature, in which he published many of his tales. On these manifold and sometimes
simultaneous labors Zschokke expended a restless and un-
tiring energy which, if concentrated upon a narrower field,
might have increased his permanent reputation. But he
lived zealously in and for his own age, and thought little of
fame, or of any form of self-interest.

His most celebrated work, however — and perhaps the
most lasting — is his *Stunden der Andacht*. At a time of
public and personal distress, in 1808, he began the issue
annonymously, as a supplement to the *Schweizerbote*, of a
weekly series of religious meditations. These were continued
for eight years, when they were collected and published,
though not till much later with avowal of their authorship.
First as separate issues, and later in book form, these papers
had a wide and influential circulation. They give a deep insight into Zschokke's profoundly religious nature, and, though
from a somewhat rationalistic point of view, are instinct
with the truest piety. This book was a favorite with Prince
Albert and Queen Victoria. After his death, and on her
behest, an English translation was made in two volumes,

I. Meditations on Life and its Religious Duties; II. Meditation on Death and Eternity. A selection from the two entitled *Meditations on Life, Death and Eternity*, has been reprinted in this country.

A small selection of "Tales by Zschokke" is included in the Tauchnitz Collection of Foreign Authors. Besides his own autobiography, *Selbstschau*, and other more extended works, pleasing sketches of Zschokke are published by his son, Emil Zschokke, by Dr. Stephen Born, and especially a *Festschrift*, by Pastor Wernly, on the unveiling of the statue at Aarau.

Our own story dates from a happy incident of Zschokke's life, and shows his most gentle and cheerful humor. At Berne in the winter 1801–2, just released from public life, Zschokke spent much time with his friends Ludwig Wieland, son of the poet, and Heinrich von Kleist, the gifted but unfortunate author of *Kätchen von Heilbronn*. One day they amused themselves by discussing an engraving in Zschokke's room, *La Cruche Cassée*, which represented a young girl and her lover standing in presence of a broken pitcher before an austere old judge. Each is trying to shield the other, while the judge's severe look adds to their confusion. It was agreed that each of the young authors should, in his own style, write his interpretation of the picture. Wieland promised a satire, Zschokke furnished the present story, and Kleist his well-known drama of the same title. Both agreed in making the judge the guilty party, and in shielding and uniting the young lovers. The work of Kleist — as he was undoubtedly the greater genius — is of higher literary rank. But Zschokke's tale is more human, and is pleasanter, or at least far easier, reading.

Der zerbrochene Krug.

———◆———

1. Mariette.

Zwar La Napoule ist nur ein ganz kleiner Ort am Meer-
busen von Cannes; aber man kennt ihn doch in der
ganzen Provence.[1] Er liegt im Schatten ewiggrüner, hoher
Palmen und dunkler Pomeranzen. Das nun macht ihn
freilich nicht berühmt. Doch sagt man, es[2] wachsen da die 5
feurigsten Weintrauben, die süßesten Rosen und die schönsten
Mädchen. Ich weiß es nicht; glaub' es indessen gern.
Schade,[3] daß La Napoule so klein ist, und der feurigen
Trauben, süßen Rosen und schönen Mädchen unmöglich genug erzeugen kann. Sonst hätte man bei uns zu Lande 10
doch auch davon.[4]

Sind[5] seit Erbauung von La Napoule alle Lanapoule-
rinnen Schönheiten gewesen, so muß ohne Zweifel die
kleine Mariette ein Wunder aller Wunder gewesen sein,
weil ihrer sogar die Chronik gedenkt.[6] Man nannte sie 15
zwar nur die kleine Mariette; doch war sie nicht kleiner,
als ungefähr ein Kind von siebenzehn Jahren und drüber
zu sein pflegt, dessen Stirn genau bis zur Lippe des auf-
gewachsenen Mannes reicht.

Die Chronik von La Napoule hatte ihre guten Gründe,
von Marietten zu erzählen. Ich, an der Stelle der Chronik,
hätte es auch gethan. Denn Mariette, die mit ihrer Mutter Manon bisher zu Avignon gewohnt hatte,[1] drehte, als
5 sie wieder in ihren Geburtsort kam, diesen beinahe ganz
um. Eigentlich nicht die Häuser, sondern die Leute und
deren Kopf; und auch wohl nicht die Köpfe aller Leute,
sondern vorzüglich solcher,[2] deren Kopf und Herz in der
Nähe von zwei seelenvollen Augen immer in großer Ge-
10 fahr sind. Ich weiß das. In solchen Fällen ist nicht zu
scherzen.[3]

Mutter Manon hätte wohl besser gethan, wäre sie in
Avignon geblieben. Aber sie machte in La Napoule eine
kleine Erbschaft; sie erhielt da ein Gütchen mit einigen
15 Weinbergen, und ein niedliches Haus im Schatten eines
Felsen, zwischen Ölbäumen und afrikanischen Akazien. So[4]
etwas schlägt keine unbemittelte Witwe aus. Nun war sie
in ihrer Meinung reich und glücklich, als wäre sie Gräfin
von Provence oder dergleichen.[5]

20 Desto schlimmer ging's mit den guten Lanapoulesen. Sie
hatten sich solchen Unheils nicht versehen, und nicht im
Homer gelesen, daß eine artige Frau ganz Griechenland
und Kleinasien in Harnisch und Zwietracht bringen konnte.[6]

Tuesday, May 12, 1907.

2. Wie das Unglück kam.

Kaum war Mariette vierzehn Tage im Hause zwischen den Ölbäumen und afrikanischen Akazien, so wußte jeder junge Lanapoulese, daß Mariette da wohne,[1] und daß in der ganzen Provence kein reizenderes Mädchen wohne, als eben in diesem Hause.

Ging sie durch den Flecken,[2] schwebend leicht, wie ein verkleideter Engel, im flatternden Rock, blaßgrünen Mieder, vorn am Busen eine Orangenblüte neben Rosenknospen, und Blumen und Bänder wehend um den grauen Hut, der ihr feines Gesicht beschattete, ja, dann wurden die finstern Alten beredt und die Jünglinge stumm. Und überall öffnete sich links und rechts ein Fensterlein, eine Thüre, der Reihe nach.[3] — „Guten Morgen," hieß es, oder „guten Abend, Mariette!" und sie nickte lächelnd rechts und links hin.[4]

Wenn Mariette in die Kirche trat, verließen alle Herzen (nämlich der Jünglinge) den Himmel, alle Augen die Heiligen,[5] und die betenden Finger verirrten sich in den Perlen der Rosenkranzschnur. Das muß gewiß oft großes Ärgernis gegeben haben, zumal den Frommen.

Zu dieser Zeit sind ohne Zweifel die jungen Mädchen von La Napoule besonders fromm gewesen, denn sie ärgerten sich am meisten. Und es war ihnen kaum zu verdenken.[6] Denn seit Mariettens Ankunft war mehr als ein Bräuti-

gam kühl geworden, und mehr als ein Anbeter seiner Geliebten abtrünnig.[1] Da gab es denn viel Zank und Vor-
würfe überall, und viele Thränen, gute Lehren und Körbe.[2]
Man sprach gar nicht mehr von Hochzeiten, sondern von
Trennungen. Man schickte sich sogar Pfänder der Treue,
Ringe und Bänder, zurück.[3] Die Alten mischten sich in
den Zank ihrer Kinder. Hader und Streit lief von Haus
zu Haus. Es war ein Jammer.

Mariette ist an allem schuld! — sagten die frommen
Mädchen; dann sagten's ihre Mütter; dann sagten's die
Väter, und zuletzt alle, sogar die jungen Männer.

Aber Mariette, in ihre Sittsamkeit und Unschuld eingehüllt,[4] wie die aufbrechende Glut der Rosenknospe in das
dunkle Grün des Blumenkelches, ahnte von dem großen
Elend nichts und blieb gütig gegen alle. — Das rührte
erst die jungen Männer, und sie sprachen: „Warum das
holde, harmlose Kind betrüben?[5] Es ist ohne Schuld!"
Dann sagten es die Väter; dann sagten es die Mütter;
und zuletzt alle, sogar die frommen Mädchen. Denn wer
mit Marietten sprach, konnte nicht anders,[6] als sie lieb-
gewinnen. Und ehe ein halbes Jahr verging, hatte jeder
mit ihr gesprochen, und war sie jedem lieb.[7] Sie aber
glaubte nicht, daß sie so geliebt werde, und hatte vorher
nicht geglaubt, daß man sie hassen könne. — Was ahnet
das dunkle, oft im Grase zertretene Veilchen,[8] wie wert es sei!

Nun wollte jeder und jede die Ungerechtigkeit gegen
Marietten abbüßen.[9] Mitleiden erhöht die Zärtlichkeit der

Zuneigung. Überall fand sich Mariette freundlicher als je gegrüßt, freundlicher angelächelt, freundlicher eingeladen zu ländlichen Spielen und Tänzen.

———◆———

3. Vom bösen Colin.

Doch nicht alle Menschen haben die Gabe des süßen Mitleids, sondern sind verstockten Herzens,[1] wie der Pharao. Dies kommt ohne Zweifel von dem natürlichen Verderben des Menschen seit dem Sündenfall; oder weil bei der Taufhandlung der Böse nicht in gehöriger Ordnung abgefertigt worden.[2]

Ein denkwürdiges Beispiel solcher Hartherzigkeit gab der junge Colin, der reichste Pächter und Gutsbesitzer in La Napoule, der seine Wein- und Ölgärten,[3] Zitronen- und Pomeranzenwälder kaum in einem Tage durchlaufen konnte. Schon dieses beweist das natürliche Verderben seines Gemütes, daß er beinahe siebenundzwanzig Jahre alt war, ohne gefragt zu haben, wozu ein Mädchen erschaffen sei.

Zwar alle Leute, besonders die weiblichen in einem gewissen Alter, darin sie gern Sünden vergeben,[4] hielten den Colin für den besten Jungen unter der Sonne. Seine Gestalt, sein frisches, unbefangenes Wesen, sein Blick, sein Lächeln hatten das Glück, besagten Leuten zu gefallen, die ihm wohl auch zur Not für eine der Sünden, die im Him-

mel schreien,[1] Ablaß gegeben hätten. Allein dem Urteil
solcher Richter ist nicht wohl zu trauen.[2]

Inzwischen[3] alt und jung zu Napoule sich mit der un-
schuldigen Mariette versöhnt hatte und sich mitleidig an
5 sie schloß, war Colin der einzige, welcher für das liebe
Kind ohne Erbarmen blieb. Brachte man das Gespräch
auf Marietten, ward er stumm, wie ein Fisch.[4] Begegnete
er ihr auf der Straße, ward er vor Zorn rot und blaß
und warf seitwärts wahrhaft verzehrende Blicke nach ihr.
10 Wenn sich abends die jungen Leute am Ufer des Meeres
bei den alten Schloßtrümmern zu fröhlichen Spielen sam-
melten, oder zu ländlichem Tanz, oder einen Wechselgesang[5]
zu beginnen, dann fehlte auch Colin nicht. Sobald aber
Mariette kam, ward der tückische Colin still, und er sang
15 um alles Gold in der Welt nicht mehr. Schade für seine
liebliche Stimme! Jeder hörte sie gern, und unerschöpflich
war er in Liedern.

Alle Mädchen sahen den bösen Colin gern, und er war
mit allen freundlich. Er hatte, wie gesagt, einen schel-
20 mischen Blick, den die Jungfrauen fürchten und lieben;
und wenn er lächelte, hätte man ihn malen sollen.[6] Aber
natürlich, die oft beleidigte Mariette sah ihn nur gar nicht
an.[7] Und da hatte sie vollkommen recht. Ob er lächelte
oder nicht, das galt ihr gleich.[8] Von seinem schelmischen
25 Blick mochte sie nur nicht reden hören;[9] und da hatte sie
abermals recht. Wenn er erzählte, und er wußte immer
viel,[10] und dann alle horchten, neckte sie ihre Nachbarinnen

und warf bald den Pierre, bald den Paul mit abgerupften
Kräutern,[1] und lachte und plauderte und hörte den Colin
nicht. Das verdroß dann den stolzen Herrn; er brach oft
mitten in der Erzählung ab und ging düster davon.

Rache ist süß. Die Tochter der Frau Manon hätte
dann wohl triumphieren können.[2] Aber Mariette war doch
ein gar zu gutes Kind, und ihr Herz zu weich. Wenn er
schwieg, that's ihr leid. Ward er traurig, verging ihr das
Lachen.[3] Entfernte er sich, mochte sie nicht lange bleiben;
und war sie zu Hause, weinte sie schönere Thränen der
Reue, als Magdalene, und hatte doch nicht halb so viel ge-
sündigt.[4]

———————◆———————

4. Der Krug.

Der Pfarrer von La Napoule, nämlich Pater Jerome,
ein Greis von siebzig Jahren, hatte alle Tugenden eines
Heiligen, und den einzigen Fehler, daß er wegen hohen
Alters sehr harthörig war. Aber dafür predigte er den
Ohren seiner Tauf- und Beichtkinder[5] desto erbaulicher, und
es hörte ihn jeder gern. Zwar predigte er beständig nur
über zwei Sätze, als wenn seine ganze Religion darin
wohnte. Entweder: „Kindlein, liebet euch[6] unter
einander;" oder: „Kindlein, die Fügungen des
Himmels sind wunderbar!" Doch wahrlich, darin lag
auch so viel Glauben, Liebe und Hoffnung, daß man damit

wohl zur Not recht selig werden könnte.[1] Die Kindlein
liebten sich ganz gehorsam unter einander und hofften auf
des Himmels Fügungen. — Nur Colin mit dem kieselharten
Herzen wollte nichts davon wissen. Selbst wenn er freund-
5 lich zu sein schien, hatte er schlimme Absichten.

   Die Napoulesen gehen gern zum Jahrmarkt der Stadt
Vence.[2] Es ist da frohes Leben, und wenn auch wenig
Geld, doch vielerlei Ware. Nun war Mariette mit Mutter
Manon auch zum Jahrmarkt; und Colin war auch da.
10 Er kaufte mancherlei Näschereien und Kleinigkeiten für seine
Freundinnen — aber für Marietten um keinen Sous.[3] Und
doch war er ihr allenthalben auf den Fersen.[4] Aber er
redete sie nicht an, und sie ihn nicht. Man sah wohl, er
brütete über Böses.

15   Da stand Mutter Manon vor einem Gewölbe still, und
sagte: „O Mariette, sieh den schönen Krug! Eine Köni-
gin dürfte sich nicht schämen,[5] ihn mit ihren Lippen zu
berühren. Sieh nur, der Rand ist strahlendes Gold, und
die Blumen daran blühen nicht schöner im Garten, und
20 sind doch nur gemalt. Und in der Mitte das Paradies!
Sieh doch nur, Mariette, wie die Äpfel vom Baume lachen;
es gelüstet einem fast.[6] Und Adam kann nicht widerstehen,
wie ihm die hübsche Eva einen zum Kosten darbietet. Und
sieh doch, wie allerliebst das Lämmchen spielend um den
25 alten Tiger hüpft, und die schneeweiße Taube mit dem
goldgrünen Halse vor dem Geier dasteht, als wollte[7] sie mit
ihm schnäbeln!"

Mariette konnte sich nicht satt sehen. „Hätt' ich solch einen Krug,[1] Mutter," sprach sie; „er ist viel zu schön, daraus zu trinken; ich würde meine Blumen darein setzen und beständig ins Paradies hinein blicken. Wir sind auf dem Markt von Vence, aber seh' ich das Bild, so ist mir,[2] als wären wir im Paradies."

So sprach Mariette, und alle Freundinnen rief sie herbei, den Krug zu bewundern; und bald standen bei den Freundinnen auch die Freunde, und endlich beinahe die halbe Einwohnerschaft von La Napoule, vor dem wunderschönen Krug. Aber wunderschön war er auch, vom allerköstlichsten, durchscheinenden Porzellan, mit vergoldeten Handhaben[3] und brennenden Farben. Schüchtern fragte man wohl den Kaufmann[4]: „Herr, wie teuer?" Und er antwortete: „Hundert Livres ist er unter Brüdern wert." Dann schwiegen sie alle und gingen.

Als keiner mehr von La Napoule vor dem Gewölbe stand, kam Colin geschlichen,[5] warf dem Kaufmann hundert Livres auf den Tisch, ließ den Krug in eine Schachtel legen, mit Baumwolle gefüllt, und trug ihn davon. Seine boshaften Plane kannte kein Mensch.

Nahe vor La Napoule,[6] auf seinem Heimwege, es war schon dunkel, begegnete er dem alten Jacques, des Richters Knecht, der vom Felde kam. Jacques war ein ganz guter Mensch, aber herzlich dumm.

„Ich will dir ein Trinkgeld geben, Jacques," sagte Colin, „wenn du diese Schachtel in Manons Haus trägst und sie

da liegen läßt.[1] Und wenn man dich bemerken oder fragen
sollte: ,Von wem kommt die Schachtel?' so sprich: ,Es
hat sie mir ein Fremdling gegeben.' Aber meinen Namen
verrate nie, sonst zürn' ich's dir ewig."[2]

5   Das versprach Jacques, nahm das Trinkgeld und die
Schachtel und ging damit dem kleinen Hause entgegen,
zwischen den Ölbäumen und afrikanischen Akazien.

—◆—

5. Der Überbringer.

Eh er dahin kam, begegnete ihm sein Herr, der Richter
Hautmartin,[3] und sprach: „Jacques, was trägst du?"

10   „Eine Schachtel für Frau Manon. Aber, Herr, ich darf
nicht sagen, von wem."

„Warum nicht?"

„Weil mir's Herr Colin ewig zürnen würde."

„Es ist gut, daß du schweigen kannst. Doch ist's schon
15 spät. Gieb mir die Schachtel; ich gehe morgen ohnehin zu
Frau Manon. Ich will ihr die Schachtel überreichen und
nicht verraten, daß sie von Colin kommt. Es spart dir
einen Weg und macht mir gutes Geschäft.[4]"

Jacques gab die Schachtel seinem Herrn, dem er ohne
20 Widerspruch in allem zu gehorchen gewohnt war. Der
Richter trug sie in sein Zimmer und betrachtete sie beim
Licht mit großer Neugier. Auf dem Deckel stand mit roter

Kreide zierlich geschrieben: „Der liebenswürdigen
und geliebten Mariette!" Herr Hautmartin wußte
aber wohl, daß dies nur Schalkheit von Colin sei und daß
eine arge Tücke dahinter laure. Darum öffnete er die
Schachtel vorsichtig, ob nicht eine Maus oder Ratte darin 5
verborgen sei.[1] Aber als er des wunderschönen Kruges
ansichtig ward,[2] den er selbst zu Vence gesehen, erschrak er
von Herzen. Denn Herr Hautmartin war in den Rechten
ein ebenso wohlerfahrener Mann, als im Unrechten.[3] Er
sah sogleich ein, Colin wolle Marietten mit dem Krug ins 10
Unglück bringen; ihn,[4] wenn er in ihren Händen wäre,
vielleicht für Geschenk eines beglückten Liebhabers aus der
Stadt oder für so etwas ausgeben, daß alle rechtlichen
Leute sich von Mariette hätten entfernen müssen.[5] Darum
beschloß Herr Hautmartin, der Richter, um allen bösen 15
Argwohn niederzuschlagen, sich selber als Geber dazu zu be-
kennen. Ohnedem hatte er Marietten lieb, und hätte gern
gesehen,[6] wenn Mariette den Spruch des greisen Pfarrers
Jerome besser gegen ihn befolgt (haben würde): „Kind=
lein, liebet euch unter einander!" Freilich, Herr 20
Hautmartin war ein Kindlein von fünfzig Jahren, und
Mariette meinte, der Spruch passe nicht mehr auf ihn.
Hingegen Mutter Manon fand, der Richter sei ein ver-
ständiges Kindlein, habe Geld und Ansehen im ganzen
Napoule, von einem Ende des Fleckens bis zum andern. 25
Und wenn der Richter von Hochzeit sprach, und Mariette
aus Furcht davon lief, blieb Mutter Manon sitzen und

fürchtete sich gar nicht vor dem langen, ehrbaren Herrn.
Auch mußte man gestehen, an seinem ganzen Leibe war
kein Fehler.   Und obwohl Colin der schönste Mann im
Flecken sein mochte,[1] hatte doch der Herr Richter in zwei
5 Dingen viel vor ihm voraus, nämlich die großen Jahre
und eine große, große Nase.   Ja, diese Nase, die dem
Richter immer wie ein Trabant vorausging,[2] seine Ankunft
zu verkünden, war ein rechter Elefant unter den mensch-
lichen Nasen.

10   Mit diesem Elefanten, seiner guten Absicht und dem
Kruge, ging der Richter folgenden Morgens in das Haus
zwischen den Ölbäumen und afrikanischen Akazien.

    „Für die schöne Mariette," sprach er, „ist mir nichts zu
kostbar.   Ihr habt[3] gestern den Krug zu Vence bewundert.
15 Erlaubt, holde Mariette, daß ich ihn und mein liebendes
Herz zu Euern Füßen lege."

    Manon und Mariette waren entzückt und erstaunt, als
sie den Krug sahen.   Manons Augen funkelten selig;[4]
aber Mariette wandte sich und sprach: „Ich darf weder
20 Euer Herz noch Euern Krug nehmen."   Da ward Mutter
Manon zornig und rief:

    „Aber ich nehme Herz und Krug an.   O du Thörin,
wie lange willst du dein Glück verschmähen?   Auf wen
wartest du?   Soll ein Graf von Provence dich zur Braut
25 machen,[5] daß du den Richter von La Napoule verachtest? —
Ich weiß besser für dich zu sorgen.   Herr Hautmartin, ich
rechne mir's zur Ehre, Euch meinen Schwiegersohn zu heißen."

Da ging Mariette hinaus und weinte bitterlich, und haßte den schönen Krug von ganzem Herzen.

Aber der Richter strich sich mit der flachen Hand über die Nase, und sprach weislich:

„Mutter Manon, übereilet nichts.[1] Das Täubchen wird[5] sich endlich bequemen, wenn es mich besser kennen lernt. Ich bin nicht ungestüm. Ich verstehe mich auf die Weiberchen,[2] und ehe ein Vierteljahr vergeht, schleich ich mich in Mariettens Herz.“

„Dazu ist seine Nase zu groß!“ flüsterte Mariette, die[10] draußen vor der Thüre horchte und heimlich lachte. In der That, es verging ein Vierteljahr, und Herr Hautmartin war noch nicht einmal mit der Nasenspitze ins Herz eingedrungen.

———

6. Die Blumen.

Aber während dieses Vierteljahrs hatte Mariette wohl[15] noch andere Geschäfte. Der Krug machte ihr viel Verdruß und Mühe; und außerdem wohl sonst noch etwas.[3]

Vierzehn Tage lang sprach man in La Napoule von nichts anderm, als dem Krug. Und jedermann sagte, es sei ein Geschenk des Richters und die Hochzeit schon verab-[20]redet.[4] Als aber Mariette feierlich allen ihren Gespielinnen erklärt hatte, sie wolle ihren Leib lieber dem Abgrunde des Meeres als dem Richter vermählen, fuhren die Mädchen

nur ärger fort, sie zu necken, sprechend: „Ach, wie selig
muß es sich ruhen[1] im Schatten seiner Nase." — Dies war
der erste Verdruß.

Dann hatte Mutter Manon den grausamen Grundsatz,
5 daß sie Marietten zwang, den Krug alle Morgen beim
Brunnen am Felsen zu schwenken und mit frischen Blumen zu füllen. Dadurch hoffte sie Marietten an den Krug
und an das Herz des Gebers zu gewöhnen. Aber sie fuhr
fort, Gabe und Geber zu hassen, und die Arbeit am Brun-
10 nen ward eine wahre Strafe für sie. Zweiter Verdruß.

Dann, wenn sie morgens zum Brunnen kam, lagen
zweimal in der Woche auf dem Felsstück daneben immerdar
einige der schönsten Blumen, schön geordnet, recht für die
Pracht des Kruges geschaffen. Und um die Blumenstengel
15 war immer ein Papierstreif geschlungen, und darauf geschrieben: „Liebe Mariette!" — Nun mußte man der
kleinen Mariette doch nicht weis machen wollen,[2] als wenn
es in der Welt noch Zauberer und Feen gäbe.[3] Folglich
kamen die Blumen und die süße Anrede derselben von
20 Herrn Hautmartin. Mariette mochte nur nicht daran
riechen, bloß weil der lebendige Atem aus des Richters
Nase sie umsäuselt hatte. Inzwischen nahm sie die Blumen, weil sie besser waren als Feldblumen, und zerriß die
Papierstreifen in tausend Stücke und streute sie auf die
25 Stelle, wo die Blumen zu liegen pflegten. Aber das
ärgerte den Richter Hautmartin gar nicht, dessen Liebe unvergleichlich groß war in ihrer Art, wie seine Nase in ihrer
Art. Dritter Verdruß.

Endlich aber entdeckte es sich im Gespräch mit Herrn Hautmartin, daß er gar nicht der Geber der Blumen wäre.[1] Wer sollte es nun sein? — Mariette war über die unverhoffte Entdeckung sehr erstaunt. Sie nahm von der Zeit an zwar die Blumen lieber[2] vom Felsen, roch auch daran, aber — wer legte sie dahin? Mariette war, was die Mädchen sonst gar nicht zu sein pflegen, sehr neugierig. Sie riet auf diesen oder jenen Jüngling von La Napoule. Doch erraten ließ sich das nicht.[3] Sie lauschte und lauerte spät hinein in die Nacht; sie stand früher auf. Aber sie erlauschte und erlauerte nichts. Und doch zweimal in der Woche des Morgens lagen immer die Wunderblumen auf dem Felsen, und auf dem darum gewundenen Papierstreifen[4] las sie immer den stillen Seufzer an sich: „Liebe Mariette!" — So etwas muß doch auch den Gleichgültigsten neugierig machen. Aber Neugier macht zuletzt brennende Pein. Vierter Verdruß.

———◆———

7. Bosheit über Bosheit.

Nun hatte am Sonntag Pater Jerome wieder über den Satz gepredigt: „Des Himmels Fügungen sind wunderbar!" Und die kleine Mariette dachte: „So wird er's auch fügen, daß ich den unsichtbaren Blumenspender endlich entdecke." Pater Jerome hatte nie unrecht.

In einer Sommernacht, da es auch allzuwarm gewesen,

war Mariette früh erwacht, und konnte nicht wieder ein-
schlafen.   Drum sprang sie freudig vom Lager, als das
erste Morgenrot über die Meereswellen und über die lerinischen Inseln[1] her gegen das Fenster des Kämmerleins
5 blitzte.   Sie kleidete sich und ging hinaus, Antlitz, Brust
und Arme am kühlen Brunnen zu waschen; den Hut nahm
sie mit, am Meere ein Stündchen zu lustwandeln.   Sie
kannte da eine heimliche Stelle zum Baden.

Um aber zu der heimlichen Stelle zu kommen, mußte
10 man über die Felsen hinter dem Hause gehen, und von da
wieder abwärts, neben Granatbüschen vorbei und Palmen.
Diesmal konnte Mariette nicht vorbei.   Denn unter der
jüngsten und schlankesten der Palmen lag im süßen Schlaf
ein junger, schlanker Mann — neben ihm ein Strauß der
15 allerschönsten Blumen.   Auch sah man wohl ein weißes
Papier daran,[2] auf welchem vermutlich wieder ein Seufzer
redete. — Wie konnte Mariette da vorbei kommen?

Sie blieb stehen und zitterte vor Schreck an allen Glie-
dern.   Dann wollte sie wieder zur Hütte heim.[3]   Kaum
20 war sie ein paar Schritte zurückgegangen, sah sie sich wieder nach dem Schläfer um und blieb stehen.   Doch aus
der Ferne ließ sich sein Gesicht nicht erkennen. — Jetzt
oder nie war ein Geheimnis zu lösen.   Sie trippelte leise
der Palme näher.   Aber er schien sich zu regen.   Nun lief
25 sie wieder zur Hütte.   Doch war seine Bewegung nichts als
furchtsame Einbildung Mariettens gewesen.   Nun machte
sie sich wieder auf den Weg zur Palme.   Allein er konnte

sich vielleicht mit seinem Schlaf verstellen.[1] Geschwind rettete
sie sich zur Hütte. Wer wird aber wegen eines leeren
Vielleichts[2] fliehen? Sie trat herzhafter die Reise zur
Palme an.

Bei diesem Schwanken ihrer schüchternen und lüsternen
Seele[3] zwischen Furcht und Neugier, bei diesem Hin= und
Hertrippeln zwischen Hütte und Palmenbaum, war sie doch
endlich dem Schläfer immer um einige kleine Schritte näher
gekommen, indem auch zugleich die Neugier siegreicher war[4]
als die Furcht.

„Was geht er mich denn an?[5] Der Weg führt mich
nur an ihm vorbei. Schlaf' er oder wach' er, ich gehe ja
nur vorbei." So dachte Manons Tochter. Aber sie ging
nicht vorbei, sondern blieb stehen; denn man mußte doch
dem Blumenspender recht ins Gesicht schauen, um seiner
Sache gewiß zu sein.[6] Zudem schlief er ja, als hätte er
seit vier Wochen keinen gesunden Schlummer gehabt. —
Und wer war's? — Nun, wer sollte es denn anders sein,
als der Erzbösewicht Colin?

Also er war's gewesen,[7] der erst aus alter Feindschaft
dem guten Mädchen so viel Todesverdruß mit dem Kruge
gemacht und es in den verdrießlichen Handel mit Herrn
Hautmartin gebracht hatte; er war's gewesen, der dann
hinging und sie mit Blumen neckte, um ihre Neugier zu
foltern. Wozu? — Er haßte Marietten. Er betrug sich
noch immer in allen Gesellschaften gegen das arme Kind
auf unverzeihliche Weise. Er wich aus, wo er konnte;

und wo er nicht konnte, betrübte er die fromme Kleine.
Gegen alle andern Mädchen von La Napoule war er ge-
sprächiger, freundlicher, gefälliger, als gegen Marietten.
Man denke![1] Er hatte sie noch nie zum Tanz aufgefor-
5 dert, und sie tanzte doch allerliebst.

Nun lag er da, verraten, ertappt. In Mariettens
Brust erwachte die Rache. Welche Schmach konnte sie ihm
anthun! — Sie nahm den Blumenstrauß, löste ihn auf,
streute mit gerechtem Zorn verächtlich sein Geschenk über
10 den Schläfer hin.[2] Nur das Papier, auf welchem wieder
der Seufzer: „Liebe Mariette!" stand, behielt sie und steckte
es geschwind in den Busen. Sie wollte für künftige Fälle
diese Probe seiner Handschrift aufbewahren. Mariette war
schlau. Nun wollte sie gehen. Aber ihre Rache schien noch
15 nicht gesättigt. Sie konnte nicht von der Stelle, ohne
Colins Bosheit mit einer ähnlichen zu strafen. Sie riß
von ihrem Hut das veilchenfarbene, seidene Band und
schlang es leise um des Schläfers Arm und um den Baum,
und knüpfte den Colin mit drei Knoten fest an die Palme.
20 Wenn er nun erwachte, wie mußte er erstaunen![3] Wie
mußte ihn die Neugier foltern, wer ihm auch den Streich
gespielt![4] — Das konnte er unmöglich erraten. Desto
besser. Es geschah ihm recht.

Mariette war noch allzugnädig gegen ihn. Ihr Werk
25 schien sie zu reuen,[5] als sie es vollbracht hatte. Ihre
Brust flog ungestüm. Ich glaube gar, es kam ihr ein
Thränchen in die Augen, mit denen sie nur allzumitleidig

den Verbrecher betrachtete. Langsam ging sie zu den Granatbüschen am Felsen zurück — sie sah sich oft um; langsam den Felsen hinauf, sie sah oft hinab nach der Palme.
Dann eilte sie zur rufenden Mutter Manon.[1]

---

8. Das Hutband.

Aber noch den gleichen Tag übte Colin neue Tücke. 5
Was that er? — Öffentlich beschämen[2] wollte er die arme
Mariette. Ach! sie hatte nicht bedacht, daß man ihr veil-
chenfarbenes Band in ganz Napoule kenne. — Colin kannte
es nur zu gut. Er schlang es stolz um seinen Hut, und
trug es vor aller Welt zur Schau, wie eine Eroberung. 10
Und jeder und jede rief:[3] „Er hat es von Marietten."
Und alle Mädchen riefen zürnend: „Der Bösewicht." Und
alle Jünglinge, die Marietten gern sahen, riefen: „Der
Bösewicht."

„Wie? Mutter Manon?" schrie der Richter Hautmartin, 15
als er zu Manon[4] kam, und er schrie so laut, daß es in
seiner ganzen Nase wunderbar wiederhallte. „Wie? Das
duldet Ihr? Meine Braut beschenkt den jungen Pächter
Colin mit einem Hutband? Es ist hohe Zeit, daß wir
unsere Hochzeit feiern. Ist die vorbei, so hab' ich auch ein 20
Recht zu reden."

„Ihr habt recht,"[5] antwortete Mutter Manon. „Wenn

die Sache so steht, muß die Hochzeit schnell sein. Ist die
vorbei, ist alles vorbei."

„Aber, Mutter Manon, Eure Tochter weigert mir noch
immer das Jawort."

5   „Rüstet nur das Hochzeitmahl."

„Aber sie will mich auch nicht einmal freundlich ansehen;
und wenn ich mich zu ihr setze, springt die kleine Wilde auf
und rennt davon."

„Herr Richter, rüstet nur das Hochzeitmahl."

10   „Aber, wenn sich Mariette sträubt?"

„Wir wollen sie überrumpeln. Wir gehen zum Pater
Jerome. Am Montag morgen in aller Früh und aller
Stille soll er die Trauung vollziehen. Das wollen wir
ihm schon beibringen.¹ Ich bin Mutter. Ihr seid die
15 erste obrigkeitliche Person in La Napoule. Er muß gehorchen. Doch Mariette darf davon nichts wissen. Am
Montag früh schicke ich sie zum Pater Jerome, ganz allein,
mit einem Auftrag, damit sie nichts ahnt.² Dann soll ihr
der Pfarrer ans Herz reden. Ein halbes Stündlein darauf
20 kommen wir beide. Dann geschwind zum Altar. Und wenn
auch Mariette da noch nein ruft, was macht's?³ Der
alte Herr kann ja nicht hören. Aber still bis dahin gegen
Marietten und ganz La Napoule."

Dabei blieb's unter den beiden.⁴ Mariette ließ sich von
25 dem Glück nicht träumen, das ihr bevorstand. Sie dachte
nur an Colins Bosheit, der sie im ganzen Orte zum Gespräch der Leute gemacht hatte. O, wie bereute sie die

Unbesonnenheit mit dem Bande! Und doch verzieh sie im
Herzen dem Bösewicht seine Schuld. Mariette war viel zu
gut. Sie sagte ihrer Mutter, sie sagte allen Gespielinnen:
„Der Colin hat mein verlorenes Hutband gefunden. Ich
hab' es ihm nicht gegeben. Nun will er mich damit ärgern. 5
Ihr wisset ja, der Colin ist mir von jeher übelan gewesen[1]
und hat immer gesucht, wie er mich kränken könnte!"

Ach, das arme Kind! es wußte nicht, auf welche neue
Abscheulichkeiten der heimtückische Mensch wieder sann.

—◆—

9. Der zerbrochene Krug.

In der Frühe trat Mariette mit dem Krug zum Brun= 10
nen. Noch lagen keine Blumen auf dem Felsstück. Es war
auch wohl zu früh; kaum stieg die Sonne aus dem Meere.

Da rauschten Tritte. Da kam Colin; in seiner Hand
die Blumen. Mariette ward blutrot im Gesicht. Colin
stammelte: „Guten Morgen, Mariette." — Aber es ging 15
ihm nicht von Herzen mit dem Gruß;[2] er konnte ihn
kaum über die Lippen bringen.

„Warum trägst du so öffentlich mein Band, Colin?"
sagte Mariette, und stellte den Krug auf das Felsstück.
„Ich gab dir's nicht."
20

„Du gabst mir's nicht, liebe Mariette?" fragte er, und
ward blaß vor innerer Wut.[3]

Mariette schämte sich ihrer Lüge, senkte die Augenlider und sagte nach einer Weile: „Wohl, ich hab' es dir gegeben; doch du sollst es nicht zur Schau tragen. Gieb mir's zurück.“

5   Da knüpfte er's langsam los; sein Ärger war so groß, daß er die Thräne im Auge nicht und nicht den Seufzer seiner Brust verbergen konnte.[1]

„Liebe Mariette, laß mir dein Band!“ sagte er leise.

„Nein!“ antwortete sie.

10   Da ging sein versteckter Grimm in Verzweiflung über. Er blickte mit einem Seufzer gen Himmel, dann düster auf Marietten, die still und fromm am Brunnen stand mit niedergeschlagenen Augen und herabhängenden Armen.

Er wand das veilchenblaue Band um den Strauß der 15 Blumen, rief: „So nimm denn alles hin!“[2] und schleuderte die Blumen so tückisch zum prächtigen Krug auf dem Felsstück, daß dieser herab zu Boden stürzte und zerbrach. Schadenfroh floh er davon.

Mutter Manon hatte alles, hinter dem Fenster lauschend, 20 gehört und gesehen. Als aber der Krug brach, verging ihr Hören und Sehen. Sie war kaum der Sprache mächtig vor Entsetzen.[3] Und als sie sich mit Gewalt zum engen Fenster hinausdrängte, dem flüchtigen Verbrecher nachzuschreien, riß sie das Fenster aus den morschen Steinen, daß 25 es mit grausenhaftem Getöse zur Erde stürzte und zerbrach.

So viel Unglück hätte jede andere Frau außer Fassung gebracht. Aber Manon erholte sich bald. „Ein Glück, daß ich Zeugin seines Frevels war!" rief sie; „er muß vor den Richter. Er soll Krug und Fenster mit seinem Golde mir aufwiegen.[1] Das giebt dir reiche Aussteuer, Mariette!" Als aber Mariette die Scherben des durchlöcherten Kruges brachte, als Manon das Paradies verloren sah,[2] den guten Adam ohne Kopf, und von der Eva nur noch die Beine fest stehend, die Schlange unverletzt triumphierend, den Tiger unbeschädigt, aber das Lämmlein bis auf den Schwanz verschwunden, als hätte es der Tiger hinuntergeschluckt, da brach Mutter Manon heulend in Verwünschungen des Colin aus und sagte: „Man sieht's wohl, der Wurf kam aus Teufels Hand."

10. Das Gericht.

Und sie nahm den Krug in der einen, Marietten an der andern Hand, und ging um die neunte Stunde zu Herrn Hautmartin, wo er zu Gericht zu sitzen pflegte.[3] Da brachte sie mit lautem Geschrei ihre Klage vor, und zeigte den zerbrochenen Krug und das verlorene Paradies. Mariette weinte bitterlich.

Der Richter, als er den Krug zerbrochen und die schöne Braut in Thränen sah, geriet in so gerechten Zorn gegen den Colin,[4] daß seine Nase veilchenblau ward, wie Mariettens berühmtes Hutband. Er ließ durch seinen Schergen alsbald den Frevler herbeiholen.[5]

Colin kam tiefbetrübt. Mutter Manon wiederholte nun ihre Klage mit vieler Beredsamkeit vor Richter, Schergen und Schreibern. Aber Colin hörte nichts. Er trat zu Marietten und flüsterte ihr zu: „Vergieb mir, liebe Mari-
5 ette, wie ich dir vergebe. Ich brach dir aus Versehen nur den Krug; du aber, du hast mir das Herz gebrochen!"

„Was soll[1] das Geflüster da?" rief mit richterlicher Hoheit Herr Hautmartin. „Höret auf Eure Anklage und verteidigt Euch."

10 „Ich verteidige mich nicht. Ich habe den Krug zerbrochen wider meinen Willen," sagte Colin.

„Das glaub' ich fast selbst," sagte schluchzend Mariette. „Ich bin so schuldig, wie er; denn ich hatte ihn beleidigt und in Zorn gebracht. Da warf er mir das Band und die
15 Blumen unvorsichtig zu. Er kann nicht dafür."[2]

„Ei, seht mir doch!"[3] schrie Mutter Manon. „Will das Mädchen noch seine Schutzrednerin sein? Herr Richter, sprechet! Er hat den Krug zerbrochen, das leugnet er nicht, und ich seinetwillen das Fenster — will er leugnen,
20 kann er's sehen."[4]

„Da Ihr nicht leugnen könnet, Herr Colin," sprach der Richter, „so zahlet Ihr für den Krug dreihundert Livres, denn so viel ist er wert; und dann für . . ."

„Nein," rief Colin, „so viel ist er nicht wert. Ich kaufte ihn
25 zu Vence auf dem Markt für Marietten um hundert Livres."

„Ihr ihn gekauft, Herr Unverschämter?" schrie der Richter, und ward im ganzen Gesichte wie Mariettens Hutband.

Doch mehr konnte er und wollte er nicht sagen, denn er
fürchtete widerliche Erörterungen in der Sache.

Aber Colin ward zornig wegen des Vorwurfs und sprach:
„Ich schickte diesen Krug am Abend des Markttages durch
Euern eigenen Knecht an Marietten. Dort steht ja Jacques 5
an der Thür. Er ist Zeuge. Jacques, rede! Gab ich dir
nicht die Schachtel, du solltest[1] sie zu Frau Manon tragen?"

Herr Hautmartin wollte dazwischen donnern,[2] aber der
einfältige Jacques sagte: „Besinnet Euch nur, Herr Richter, Ihr nahmet mir Colins Schachtel ab und trugt, was 10
darin gewesen, zur Frau Manon. Die Schachtel liegt ja
dort noch unter den Papieren."

Da mußten die Schergen den einfältigen Jacques hin-
auswerfen; und auch Herr Colin ward hinausgewiesen, bis
man ihn wieder rufen werde.[3]   15

„Ganz wohl, Herr Richter," entgegnete Colin, „aber dies
Stückchen soll Euer letztes in Napoule sein. Ich weiß wohl
mehr als dies,[4] daß Ihr Euch mit meinem Eigentum bei
Frau Manon und Marietten in Gunst setzen wolltet.[5]
Wenn Ihr mich sucht, so werdet Ihr wohlthun, nach Grasse 20
zum Herrn Landvogt zu reisen."[6] Damit ging Colin.

Herr Hautmartin war über den Handel sehr verwirt
und wußte in der Bestürzung nicht, was er that. Frau
Manon schüttelte den Kopf. Die Sache war ihr ganz
dunkel und verdächtig worden.[7] „Wer wird mir nun den 25
zerbrochenen Krug zahlen?" fragte sie.

„Mir," sagte Mariette mit glühendem Angesichte, „mir ist
er beinah' schon bezahlt."

11. Wunderbare Fügungen.

Colin ritt noch gleichen Tages nach Grasse zum Herrn
Landvogt und kam andern Morgens in der Frühe zurück.
Herr Hautmartin aber lachte nur dazu und redete der
Frau Manon allen Argwohn aus,[1] und schwor, er wolle sich
5 die Nase abschneiden lassen, wenn Colin nicht dreihundert
Livres für den zerbrochenen Krug zahlen müsse. — Auch
ging er mit Frau Manon zum Pater Jerome wegen der
Trauung und schärfte ihm wohl ein, Marietten ernsthaft
ihre Pflicht vorzustellen, als gehorsame Tochter dem Willen
10 der Mutter und der Vermählung nicht zu widerstreben.
Das versprach auch der alte, fromme Herr, obwohl er nur
die Hälfte von allem verstand, was man ihm ins Ohr schrie.

Aber Mariette nahm den zerbrochenen Krug in ihre Schlaf-
kammer und hatte ihn nun erst recht lieb,[2] und ihr war,
15 als wäre das Paradies in ihre Brust eingezogen, seit es
auf dem Krug durchlöchert worden.

Als nun der Montag Morgen kam, sprach Mutter
Manon zu ihrer Tochter: „Kleide dich wohl an und trage
dieses Myrtenkränzlein zum Pater Jerome; er verlangt es
20 für eine Braut." — Mariette kleidete sich sonntäglich, nahm
ohne Arg den Myrtenkranz und trug ihn zum Pater Jerome.

Unterwegs begegnete ihr Colin, der grüßte sie freundlich
und schüchtern;[3] und als sie sagte, wohin sie den Kranz
trage, sprach Colin: „Ich gehe den gleichen Gang, denn ich

muß dem Pfarrer das Geld bringen für den Kirchenzehnten."
Und wie sie beide gingen, nahm er schweigend ihre Hand;
da zitterten beide, als hätten sie gegen einander große Ver=
brechen auf dem Gewissen.

„Hast du mir vergeben?" flüsterte ängstlich Colin. „Ach, 5
Mariette, was hab' ich dir gethan, daß du so grausam gegen
mich bist?"

Aber sie konnte nichts sagen, als: „Sei nur ruhig, Co=
lin, das Band sollst du wieder haben. Und ich will deinen
Krug behalten. Gelt,[1] er ist doch von dir?" 10

„Mariette, kannst du zweifeln? Sieh, was ich habe, dir
möcht' ich alles geben. Willst du mir künftig freundlich
sein, wie andern?"

Sie antwortete nicht. Als sie aber in das Pfarrhaus
traten, blickte sie ihn seitwärts an, und da sie seine schönen 15
Augen naß sah, lispelte sie ihm zu: „Lieber Colin!" —
Da bog er sich und küßte ihre Hand. Da ging die Thüre
eines Zimmers auf, und Pater Jerome in ehrwürdiger
Gestalt stand vor ihnen. — Die jungen Leute waren wie
vom Schwindel befallen, denn sie hielten fest, eins am an= 20
dern.[2] Ich weiß nicht, war das die Wirkung des Handkusses,
oder die Ehrfurcht vor dem Greis?

Da reichte Mariette dem Pfarrer das Myrtenkränzchen.
Er legte es auf ihr Haupt und sprach: „Kindlein, liebet
euch unter einander!" und redete nun dem guten Mäd= 25
chen auf das beweglichste und rührendste zu,[3] den Colin zu
lieben. Denn der alte Herr hatte wegen seiner Harthörig=

keit den Namen des Bräutigams entweder falsch gehört,
oder wegen des alternden Gedächtnisses vergessen, und
meinte, Colin müsse der Bräutigam sein.

Da brach unter dem Zuspruch des Greises Mariettens
5 Herz, und mit Thränen und Schluchzen rief sie: „Ach, ich
lieb' ihn ja schon lange,[1] aber er hasset mich.“

„Ich dich hassen, Mariette?“ rief Colin; „meine Seele
lebte nur in dir, seit du nach La Napoule gekommen. O
Mariette, wie konnte ich denn hoffen und glauben, daß du
10 mich liebtest? Betet dich nicht ganz La Napoule an?“

„Warum flohst du mich, Colin, und zogest alle meine
Gespielen[2] mir vor?“

„O Mariette, ich ging in Furcht und Zagen, in Kummer
und Liebe unter, wenn ich dich sah. Ich hatte den Mut
15 nicht, dir nahe zu sein; und war ich nicht bei dir, war ich
noch unglückseliger.“

Als sie so gegen einander redeten, meinte der gute Pater,
sie haderten. Und er legte seine Arme um beide, führte sie
zusammen und sprach flehend: „Kindlein, Kindlein,
20 liebet euch unter einander.“

Da sank Mariette an Colins Brust, und Colin schlug
beide Arme um sie, und beider Antlitz strahlte in stummer
Entzückung. Sie vergaßen den Pfarrer, die ganze Welt.
Colins Lippe hing an Mariettens süßem Munde. Beide
25 hatten so ganz ihre Besinnung verloren, daß sie, ohne es
zu wissen, dem entzückten Pater Jerome in die Kirche folg-
ten vor den Altar.

„Mariette!" seufzte er.

„Colin!" seufzte sie.

In der Kirche beteten viele Andächtige;[1] aber mit Erstaunen wurden sie Zeugen von Colins und Mariettens Vermählung. Viele liefen noch vor Beendigung der Feierlichkeit hinaus, es links und rechts in Napoule verkünden zu können: Colin und Mariette sind vermählt!

Als die Trauung vollbracht war, freute sich Pater Jerome redlich, daß es ihm so gut gelungen[2] und von den Brautleuten so wenig Widerstand geleistet war. Er führte sie ins Pfarrhaus.

---

12. Ende dieser merkwürdigen Geschichte.

Da kam atemlos Mutter Manon. Sie hatte zu Hause lange auf die Ankunft des Bräutigams gehofft. Er war nicht gekommen. Beim letzten Glockengeläute hatte die Angst sie getrieben, und sie selbst sich auf den Weg zu Herrn Hautmartin gemacht.[3] Dort aber war neues Entsetzen über sie gekommen. Sie erfuhr, der Herr Landvogt nebst den Dienern der Viguerie sei erschienen,[4] habe Rechnungen, Kassen und Protokolle des Richters in Untersuchung genommen, dann den Herrn Hautmartin in der gleichen Stunde verhaften lassen.[5]

„Das hat gewiß der gottlose Colin gestiftet!" war ihr Gedanke. Nun hatte sie sich eilfertig zum Pfarrhaus be-

geben, um beim Pater Jerome den Aufschub der Trauung
zu entschuldigen.   Da trat ihr lächelnd, und mit Stolz auf
5 sein Werk, der gute Greis entgegen, und an seinen Händen
das neuvermählte Paar.

Jetzt verlor Frau Manon in vollem Ernst Gedanken und
Sprache, als sie das Vorgefallene vernahm.[1] Aber Colin
hatte der Gedanken und Sprache jetzt mehr[2] als sonst in
10 seinem ganzen Leben. Er fing von seiner Liebe an und dem
zerbrochenen Kruge und von des Richters Falschheit, und wie
er diesen Ungerechten zu Grasse in der Viguerie entlarvt habe.
Dann bat er um Mutter Manons Segen, weil es nun geschehen sei, ohne daß Mariette noch er daran schuld waren.[3]

15   Pater Jerome, der lange nicht verstand, was geschehen
sei,[4] faltete, als er über die Vermählung durch Mißverständnis den vollsten Aufschluß empfangen, die Hände fromm und
rief mit emporgehobenem Blick: „Wunderbarlich[5] sind
des Himmels Fügungen.“ — Colin und Mariette küß-
20 ten ihm die Hände; Mutter Manon, aus bloßer Ehrfurcht
vor dem Himmel, gab dem jungen Ehepaar ihren Segen,
bemerkte aber zwischenein, der Kopf sei ihr wie umgedreht.

Frau Manon war ihres Schwiegersohnes froh, als sie
seinen Reichtum kennen lernte, und besonders da Herr Haut-
25 martin gefangen, samt seiner Nase, nach Grasse geführt ward.

Der zerbrochene Krug aber ward in der Familie bis auf
den heutigen Tag als Andenken und Heiligtum aufbewahrt.[6]

NOTES

NOTES.

I.

Page 1. — 1. The scene is laid in the south of France. Cannes is an important town in the Department of Var, on the Mediterranean. Here Napoleon landed on his return from Elba, March 1, 1815. La Napoule is a small village on the bay, a few miles distant. The old Provence (Lat. *provincia*) is now subdivided into departments; yet the name is still used. The region is famed for the beauty of its climate and the richness of its fruits and foliage.

Observe that most of the proper names herein are French (see Vocabulary).

2. **es**, introductory: *there grow there.* — **glaub' es,** for **ich glaub' es,** is colloquial.

3. **Schade**, elliptical: (it is) pity. — **der Trauben,** etc., depending on **genug.**

4. **bei uns zu Lande,** phrase: *in our country* — we should also doubtless have some of them.

5. **Sind,** etc., the inversion marks condition: *if,* etc.

6. **ihrer,** gen. dep. on **gedenkt.** The "chronicle" is, of course, only a playful fiction.

Page 2. — 1. **Avignon,** an important city on the Rhone, of great antiquity and historical interest, at times the residence or refuge of the Popes. — **drehte . . . um,** (**umdrehen**).

2. **solcher, deren,** a frequent connection: *of those whose heads,* etc. Note singular **Kopf,** English plural; also two senses of **deren.**

3. **ist nicht zu scherzen,** impersonal infin. idiom: *there is no joking;* **es** (see **1,** 2) is omitted in consequence of inversion.

4. **So etwas,** *such a thing.* — **schlägt . . . aus** (**ausschlagen**). Note also the phrase **Erbschaft machen,** *to receive a legacy.*

5. **dergleichen** (of the like): *something of the kind.* — **als wäre,** condition (**wenn** omitted): *as if she were,* etc.

33

6. **eine artige Frau,** the Grecian Helen, cause of the Trojan War, the subject of Homer's Iliad. Note the phrase **ging's mit,** it fared with, *it was for,* etc.

II.

Page 3. — 1. **wohne,** subj. indirect, in same tense as would have been used by the persons referred to. — **vierzehn Tage,** *a fortnight.*

2. **Ging sie,** as **1,** 5 : *if* or *when she went.* — **Orangenblüte,** the descriptive accusative.

3. **der Reihe nach,** phrase : *one after another.*

4. **hin,** along; that is, as she went along. — **hieß es,** impersonal: *was the word.*

5. **die Heiligen,** figures of saints on the altar, etc. — **Rosenkranz- schnur,** *rosary,* a string of beads, pearls, balls, etc., originally cut in form of *roses,* used for counting prayers: *the fingers went astray,* or *lost the count.*

6. **war . . . zu verdenken,** infin. idiom, as **2,** 3 : *they could hardly be blamed for it.*

Page 4. — 1. **abtrünnig** (abtrennen); **seiner Geliebten** is dative.

2. **Körbe,** familiar; our "mittens": **einen Korb geben, bekommen,** " to give, *or* get, the mitten."

3. **Man schickte sich,** reflexive as reciprocal : *each other,* **sich** indirect object.

4. **in ihre Sittsamkeit . . . eingehüllt,** *wrapt in.* Note the accus.

5. **betrüben,** the absolute infin., as in English : *why trouble?* etc. Note the neut. pron. **es,** *she ;* also the humor: the girls, who were the first to accuse, are the last to acquit, and *vice versa* for the young men.

6. **anders als,** else than, i.e. *could not help,* etc.

7. **und war sie,** a rather unusual order. In the familiar style of this text, freedom in word order often occurs. Note the indirect subjunctives, **werde, könne, sei,** as **3,** 1, and hereafter.

8. **Was ahnet,** *what suspicion has the dark violet, often trampled in the grass,* etc., the participle, with its attributes, preceding the noun.

9. **Nun wollte** ; note singular verb, very frequent with several singular subjects, even when they do not, as line 7 above, express a combined idea, and especially when the subjects follow the verb; also the force of the inflections in **jeder und jede.**

III.

Page 5. — 1. **verſtockten Herzens**, predicate gen. "And the Lord hardened the heart of Pharaoh." Gen. xiv, 8. — i.e. *but some are*, etc.

2. **abgefertigt worden** (iſt), note the omission.

3. **Wein- und Ölgärten** = **Weingärten und Ölgärten.**

4. **darin**, here relat. = **worin.** — **gewiß**, like our *certain*, is here indefinite; as in our phrase "of *uncertain* age."

Page 6. — 1. **die im Himmel ſchrein**; we say: cry to heaven. — **gegeben hätten**, *would have given;* the condition implied in **zur Not**, *in case of need.*

2. **dem Urteil**, impers. as heretofore; infin. in pass. sense: *the judgment is not to be trusted;* or: there's no trusting, etc. See **3**, 6; but **es** omitted, as **2**, 3.

3. **Inzwiſchen**, here conj. *while.* — **alt und jung**, absolute forms, indecl. in familiar style. Note again sing. verb. — **ſich . . . ſchloß**, *made friends with her.* — **Napoule**, for La Napoule, *la* being French article.

4. **Brachte man**, conditional, as **3**, 2, etc. — **ward er** = ſo ward er.

5. **Wechſelgeſang**, a "round," in which alternate parts are sung by different voices, often with a general chorus.

6. **hätte . . . malen ſollen**, *he should have been painted.* For the form, **ſollen** for geſollt after infinitive, see grammar.

7. **ſah . . . an** (anſehen), *did not even look at him.*

8. **galt . . . gleich**, phrase: *was all the same to her.*

9. **mochte . . . reden hören**, infin. idiom: *did not like even to hear talk of.* — In **recht haben**, recht is really a noun, yet, as in other like forms (leid thun, etc.) now written without capital.

10. **wußte viel**, i.e. zu erzählen, *had much* (many stories) *to tell.*

Page 7. — 1. **mit abgerupften Kräutern**, with pulled up weeds, i.e. *pulled up weeds and pelted*, etc. Participles and adjectives have more flexible construction in German than in English. See hereafter.

2. **hätte . . . können**, *might well have triumphed* (as **6**, 6).

3. **verging ihr** (dat.) **das Lachen**, *her laughter ceased.*

4. **Magdalene**, the penitent Mary Magdalene of the New Testament, the traditional type, in art, of penitence and beauty.

IV.

5. For **Tauf= und Beichtkinder** (children in baptism and in the confessional), we have no corresponding terms. — **es hörte ;** es is, again, purely introductory, here not translatable (see **1,** 2).

6. **liebet euch,** as 4, 3, **unter einander** adding emphasis. — **wohnte** is subjunctive of condition.

Page 8. — 1. **Selig** refers usually to the blessedness of the dead; here : *might win complete salvation.* — **zur Not . . . könnte,** as 6, 1. — Note, l. 4, **wollte . . . wissen,** *took no notice of the matter.*

2. **Jahrmarkt,** annual fair, formerly more common than now.　Vence is a town in the adjacent department of Alpes Maritimes.

3. **um keinen Sous,** not for a sou, *not a sou's worth.*　The *sou* is an old French coin = about one cent.　(The final *s,* here incorrectly added, is silent.)

4. **ihr . . . auf den Fersen.**　Note the personal dat., our possessive.

5. **dürfte . . . schämen,** *need not be ashamed.*

6. **es gelüstet einem,** *it almost makes one's mouth water.*　Such pictures were very common on old-time crockery, tapestry, etc. — In **sieh doch nur,** note the expressive particles : *do just look.*

7. **als wollte,** as 2, 5 ; **wollte** is subjunctive.

Page 9. — 1. **Hätt' ich,** etc. — The construction here begun is broken off, and resumed as independent, in **ich würde,** below.　Thus the condition has optative force : *I wish I had,* etc.

2. **so ist mir,** it seems to me, *I feel as if.*

3. **Handhaben.**　The title of this story is usually translated "The Broken Pitcher"; but it here appears that the **Krug** had two handles, and (l. 3 above) was to be used for drinking; hence, rather, a *goblet* or *jar.*　The word **Krug** is used for almost any earthen vessel.

4. **fragte man wohl ; wohl** gives indefinite sense : *one would ask.* — **unter Brüdern,** *among brothers,* i.e. at the lowest terms.

5. **kam . . . geschlichen,** part. idiom with **kommen** : *came creeping up.* — **ließ . . . legen,** *had* (caused to be) *laid.*　Note the idioms : the p. part. **geschlichen** regards the completion, not the progress, of the action : *came, having crept up.*　The infin. **legen** implies an unexpressed subject.

6. **Nahe vor,** that is, *just before reaching.* — **Jacques,** French, *James* (pronounce Zchäk).

Page 10. — 1. **liegen läßt**, *leave . . . lying*. Compare with **9, 5**, above; and note the contracted läßt for läffeft. See grammar.

2. **zürn ich's dir;** es is direct object: *I'll never forgive you for it*, with reversed objects, as frequently. Note again present as future.

V.

3. **Hautmartin,** French. Pronounce Hômarti*n* (n nasal).

4. **gutes Geschäft,** here: *a good excuse.*

Page 11. — 1. **ob nicht,** etc., that is, *to see whether*, etc. Note again tense of indirect subjunctives.

2. **ansichtig ward,** taken together: *caught sight of*, with genitive; ward was more common in earlier prose than now. — For **gesehen (hatte)** compare **5, 2**; so only in transposed order.

3. **Rechten . . . Unrechten.** Here is a play on words, difficult to translate. In den Rechten (plur.) means *in the law* generally; im Unrechten, *in the unlawful*, in crime, etc.

4. **ihn** (i.e. den Krug) **. . . ausgeben,** dep. on wolle. — **wenn er . . . wäre,** *when it should be*, contingent subjunctive.

5. **hätten entfernen müssen,** *would* (if this were true) *have had to*, etc. Note the idiomatic forms, as **7, 2**, etc.

6. **hätte gern gesehen,** *would have been glad*. Note the less usual conditional, **haben würde,** for hätte.

Page 12. — 1. **sein mochte,** *might be*, the indicative concedes the fact. — **hatte . . . voraus,** *had the advantage over him.*

2. **Trabant,** body guard, attendant on royal personages. — **ein rechter Elefant,** as we say: "a *regular* elephant."

3. **Ihr habt;** the second plural of courteous address, much more usual formerly than now. In this sense the capital initial is often used to distinguish from the genuine plural.

4. **funkelten selig,** *sparkled with delight.*

5. **zur Braut machen,** factitive idiom: *make you his bride.*

Page 13. — 1. **übereilet nichts,** *don't be in too much of a hurry.* In following, note again the grammatical gender es, as **5, 1**.

2. **verstehe mich auf,** *I know all about.* — **Weiberchen** is used with playful familiarity.

VI.

3. **außerdem,** etc., i.e. machte ihr Verdruß, etc., as will appear below. Note the cumulated particles, **wohl sonst noch,** often impossible to translate verbally.

4. **die Hochzeit (sei) schon verabredet,** a rather strong ellipsis, here to avoid repetition (not as **11,** 2, etc.).

Page 14. — 1. **muß es sich ruhen,** corresponding to the impers. es ruht sich : *how delightful must it be to rest.* — **fuhren . . . fort** (fortfahren).

2. **nun mußte . . . wollen** (as **6,** 9), now surely one need not try to impose on, as if, i.e., *no one need try to make M. believe that,* etc. In weis machen (also written weismachen), *to make believe* (falsely), weis is referred to wissen, yet often written weiß (= white), as if *to whitewash, gloss over.*

3. **als wenn es . . . gäbe** (impers.) *as if there were,* unreal condition.

Page 15. — 1. **wäre,** indirect, for the more usual sei.

2. **lieber,** *more willingly* — than before.

3. **erraten,** note emphatic position, and infin. idiom with lassen : *that could not be guessed.* See **9,** 5. Note also the force of **er–,** here and below. — **stand . . . auf** (aufstehen).

4. **auf dem darum gewundenen P.** Such forms usually require transposition : *on the strip of paper (that was) wound around it.*

VII.

Page 16. — 1. **die lerinischen Inseln,** the Lérins — Lerinian Isles — a group of small islands near the coast of Var. On one of them, St. Marguerite, the "Man with the Iron Mask," was confined. — **her,** as frequently (like hin), is here not translatable.

2. **Auch sah man wohl ;** wohl, here hardly translatable, implies : as was to be expected. The force of such "particles," in which German abounds, is often difficult to render, except, partly, by emphasis. Note the condensed figure in **ein Seufzer redete.**

3. **wollte . . . heim** (gehen), frequent ellipsis with modal verbs. — **sah . . . um** (umsehen). — Note also infin. with blieb.

Page 17. — 1. **konnte ſich . . . verſtellen,** *might have been sham-*
ming. Note the tense forms.

2. **Vielleichts,** as noun: *a mere perhaps,* a bare possibility. — **trat**
. . . an (antreten).

3. **ſchüchternen und lüſternen.** Note the assonance, very common
in German phrases. We might render: *bashful and wishful.*

4. **ſiegreicher . . . als** is a "pregnant" expression, including **ſtärker**
als, and **ſiegreich über.**

5. **Was geht . . . an** (angehen), what has he to do with me, *how*
does he concern me?

6. **ſeiner Sache gewiß,** phrase: *to be certain of the* (one's) *matter.* —
ſchlief er ja. **ja** is here purely emphatic: *just* as if, etc. So, **denn,**
l. 18: who else, *do you suppose?* etc. Such "particles," or "exple-
tives," require close attention.

7. **Alſo er war's geweſen,** emphatic position of **er.** Note, following, that **Mädchen** is first represented by **es,** then by **ſie, ihre;** the latter
form being more usual when farther separated from the noun.

Page 18. — 1. **Man denke!** *Only think!*

2. **über den Schläfer hin.** See **her, 16,** 1; or **hin** may be taken as
part of sep. verb **hinſtreuen,** without change of sense.

3. The tenses **erwachte, mußte,** etc., are viewed, by a lively figure,
from the future, as if the facts (in M's mind) were already real: *when*
he waked up, how astonished he must have been, etc.

4. **wer . . . auch,** dep. on **Neugier:** (as to) who ever, *who in the*
world.

5. **ihr Werk** is subject, the idiom being impersonal. English: *she*
seemed to repent of. — **vollbracht** (vollbringen).

Page 19. — 1. **rufenden,** as **15,** 4, etc.: *who was calling her.*

VIII.

2. **beſchämen,** emphatic position as **15,** 2 — can be rendered here
only by emphasis.

3. **jeder und jede.** Note again the condensation, due to inflection.

4. **zu Manon,** means *to her house;* but below, p. **20,** l. 7, **zu ihr,** *by*
her (side).

5. In **Ihr habt recht, recht** is really noun, but without capital, as now
usually in such phrases.

Page 20. — 1. **ihm ... beibringen,** with reversed objects, we may say: *bring him to it.* See **10,** 2. — **schon,** emphatic: *never fear.*

2. **damit ... ahnt,** we should rather expect subjunctive; but this form is frequent; **damit = so daß**; as if the purpose were already real. — **aus Herz reden,** *appeal to her,* bring the matter home to her heart.

3. **was macht's,** *what matter?* — **ja,** *you know.* — **still,** elliptical, *silence!*

4. **Dabei blieb's,** *there the matter rested.* — **ließ ... träumen,** simply = träumte.

Page 21. — 1. **übelan** seems to be only emphatic for **übel,** a popular expression perhaps: *has from the first been mean to me.* — **ja,** as before, emphatic, assumes the truth of the statement: *you know, don't you?*

IX.

2. **es ging ihm,** etc., impers. phrase: *the greeting came not,* etc. Note frequency of impersonal and reflexive forms in German.

3. **vor innerer Wut ... sein Ärger ... versteckter Grimm.** These expressions are of course ironical, playfully implying really quite different feelings.

Page 22. — 1. **daß er die Thräne ... nicht und nicht den Seufzer.** Note the contrasted order. The text abounds in such felicities of style.

2. **nimm ... hin,** as **18,** 2. Likewise **floh ... davon** may represent davon fliehen, or davonfliehen. Usage varies.

3. **der Sprache mächtig,** gen. object, as **11,** 2. — **verging ihr,** as **7,** 3: *she lost the power of hearing,* etc.

Page 23. — 1. **mir aufwiegen,** weigh up, where we say: *weigh down.* **mir** is the *ethical* dative: pay me their weight in gold. — **muß vor,** as **16,** 3.

2. **das Paradies verloren** is, of course, a play upon the title of Milton's "Paradise Lost." — **brach ... aus** (ausbrechen).

X.

3. **zu Gericht,** *in court,* as judge. — **brachte ... vor** (vorbringen).

4. **gegen den Colin.** The article with personal names has often a contemptuous, or merely a familiar sense. See line 10 above.

5. **ließ ... herbeiholen,** as **9,** 5.

Page 24. — 1. **Was soll**, *what is the meaning of.* Here again **Eure, Euch**, in formal address, as **12,** 3. Usage varies as to the capital.

2. **kann nicht dafür**, phrase: *is not responsible for it.* — **warf . . . zu** (zuwerfen).

3. **seht mir doch**, again the "ethical" dative, often hardly translatable; **doch** is emphatic and indignant.

4. **will er . . . kann er**, as **6,** 4; so, frequently, in simple style. — Note the forms **höret, könnet, zahlet**, spoken with judicial formality.

Page 25. — 1. **du solltest**, subj. indirect, implies *saying that*, etc.

2. **dazwischen donnern**, *to thunder an interruption.*

3. **bis . . . werde**, subj. indirect, in the tense of the speaker: *until he should* (shall) *be recalled.*

4. **daß**, etc., defines **dies**: more than this (simple fact) that, etc.

5. **in Gunst setzen . . . bei**, to win the favor of, *curry favor with.*

6. **zum Herrn Landvogt**, the French préfet, local commissioner, or *provost.* The titular **Herr** is often untranslated. Grasse is the capital of the department of Alpes Maritimes.

7. **worden** = geworden, only in poetic or colloquial style.

XI.

Page 26. — 1. **redete . . . aus** (ausreden), talked out of her; we should say, with reversed objects: *talked her out of.* See **10,** 2.

2. **hatte nun erst . . . lieb**, *now for the first time* (only now) *loved it right dearly.* For **ihr war, als**, see **9,** 2.

3. **der grüßte ;** here not relative, but may be so rendered. This form is frequent, in simple style.

Page 27. — 1. **Gelt** (from subj. of gelten), as interjection, implies a wish that something may be true. — **doch**, *after all* (as I thought).

2. **eins**, the neuter includes both sexes.

3. **auf das =ste**, the adverbial superl. absolute. **redete . . . zu** (zureden).

Page 28. — 1. **liebe . . . schon lange**, *have long loved.* Note tense idiom; also absolute infin. **hassen**, as **4,** 5.

2. **Gespielen**, here = Gespielinnen. — **zogest . . . vor** (vorziehen).

Page 29. — 1. **beteten,** as is usual, at all hours, in Catholic churches. Note the strong form **Andächtige** (here *worshipers*).

2. **ihm . . . gelungen,** impers. idiom : *that he had succeeded so well.*

XII.

3. **und sie gemacht;** supply **hatte,** as **13,** 4 : *had herself started.*

4. **Viguerie** (French), court of a *Viguier* or local judge.

5. **lassen** belongs to **habe** ; the form as **11,** 5 ; sense as **9,** 5.

Page 30. — 1. **das Vorgefallene,** *what had happened.* In consequence of their inflection, adjectives and participles have (as already remarked, **7,** 1, etc.) much more flexible construction than in English. Hence also their freer use as nouns.

2. **der Gedanken,** etc., depends on **mehr** ; as **1,** 3.

3. **ohne daß . . . waren,** *without . . . being to blame for it.* Compare **ohne zu, 28,** 3, and note idiomatic forms, the subject here being changed. Note also **noch,** *nor,* corresponding to negative **ohne.**

4. **was geschehen sei** ; we might rather expect **war** ; on the other hand, in line 12, **wären** (or **seien**). The mood marks often only the point of view, with large freedom of choice. See **20,** 2. — This sentence is also instructive as to the position of subordinate clauses.

5. **wunderbarlich** is a humorous form, made up of **wunderbar** and **wunderlich,** neither of which sufficed for the old man's emotion.

6. **ward . . . aufbewahrt,** our idiom here requires the perfect : *has been,* etc. Note again use of **ward,** more frequently than now.

VOCABULARY

VOCABULARY.

This Vocabulary, being made for early reading, is intended to contain all the words of the text, except a few of the most common grammatical forms. Separable prefixes of verbs, and other compounds when occurring under a common title, are indicated by = ; affixes of derivation by –. Obvious compounds and derivatives are included under a leading title whenever possible without violating the alphabetical order. The sign — means repetition of the title word. Grammatical inflections are indicated whenever not regular, under the most general rules, and verb forms are given whenever they include any vowel change; but such forms, when occurring as primitives, are not repeated for compounds. Accents are indicated only when foreign or otherwise unusual. S indicates strong verbs, M, mixed (including modal) verbs. The sign ͧ shows vowel modification in inflection or derivation.

---

ab, off, down, away.
  =**brechen,** *S.* to break off.
  =**büßen,** to expiate, atone for.
Abend, *m.* –e, evening; **abends,** in the evening.
aber, but, however; =**mals,** again.
ab=fertigen, to dispose of, get rid of.
Abgrund, *m.* ͧe, abyss, bottom.
Ablaß, *m.* remission, indulgence.
ab=nehmen, *S.* to take off, take away.
  =**rupfen,** to pluck off.
Abscheu'lichkeit, *f.* horror.
ab=schneiden, *S.* to cut off.
Absicht, *f.* view, purpose.
abtrünnig, faithless, recreant.
abwärts, down, downwards.
ab=weisen, *S.* to refuse, repulse.
afrikan'isch, African.
ahnen, to forebode, guess.

ähnlich, like, similar.
Aka'zie, *f.* acacia (tree).
all, all, every, any.
allein, alone, only; *conj.* but, yet.
allenthalben, everywhere.
aller=köstlichst, most precious.
  =**liebst,** most charming, dearest.
  =**schönst,** most beautiful.
allzu=gnädig, too kind.
  =**mitleidig,** too pitiful.
  =**warm,** too warm, very warm.
als, as, than, but; *conj.* as if.
  =**bald,** immediately.
also, so, then, accordingly.
alt, ͧ, old, ancient.
Altar', *m* ͧe, altar.
Alter, *n.* age, old age.
altern, to grow old, age.
am = an dem.

NOTE. — The noun plurals here assumed as regular, "under the most general rules," are: *Masc.* and *Neut.* of Class I (pl. —), *Masc. Monosyllables* (—e), *Masc.* —e, or final accent (—(e)n), *Neuter Monosyllables* (ͧer), *Feminines* (–(e)n). Departures from these forms are recorded.

45

an, *adv.* on; *prep.* on, at, in, to, of.
an=beten, to adore; –er, adorer.
　=blicken, to look at.
andächtig, devout, pious.
Andenken, *n.* memory, memorial.
ander, other, second, next.
anders, otherwise, else.
an=fangen, *S.* to begin.
　=gehen, *S.* to begin, concern.
Angesicht, *n.* -er, face.
Angst, *f.* "e, anxiety, fear.
ängstlich, anxious, fearful.
Anklage, *f.* accusation.
an=kleiden, to clothe, dress.
Ankunft, *f.* "e, arrival.
an=lachen, =lächeln, to smile on.
an=nehmen, *S.* to accept, receive.
Anrede, *f.* address, speech.
an=reden, to speak to, address.
ans = an das.
an=schließen, *S.* to attach to, annex.
　=sehen, *S.* to look at, behold.
Ansehen, *n.* regard, dignity.
ansichtig, in sight of.
an=thun, *S.* to put on, do (to).
Antlitz, *n.* face.
an=treten, *S.* to step on, begin.
antworten, to answer.
Apfel, *m.* ", apple.
Arbeit, *f.* labor, work.
arg, ", bad, mean.
Arg, *m. see* Argwohn.
Ärger, *m.* vexation, anger.
ärgern, to vex, anger; *reflex.* to be angry, get angry.
Ärgernis, *n.* vexation, anger, offence.

Argwohn, *m.* suspicion.
arm, ", poor.
Art, *f.* kind, manner, way.
artig, pretty, polite, good.
Atem, *m.* breath; –los, breathless.
auch, also, too, even.
auf, *adv.* up, open; *prep.* up, upon, on, to, for, against, *etc.*
auf=bewahren, to keep, preserve.
　=brechen, *S.* to break up, open.
　=fordern, to summon, invite.
　=gehen, *S.* to rise, open.
　=lösen, to solve, dissolve.
Aufschluß, *m.* "e, explanation.
Aufschub, *m.* delay, postponement.
auf=springen, *S.* to spring up, fly open.
　=stehen, *S.* to stand up, rise, get up.
Auftrag, *m.* "e, commission, business.
auf=wachsen, *S.* to grow up.
　=wiegen, *S.* to outweigh.
Auge, *n.* -s, –n, eye; –n=lid, *n.* eyelid.
aus, *adv.* out; *prep.* out of, from, of, by, *etc.*
aus=brechen, *S.* to break out.
　=geben, *S.* to give out, represent.
　=reden, to talk out (of).
　=schlagen, *S.* to strike out, reject, refuse.
außer, out of, without, besides, except; =dem, besides, moreover.
Aussteuer, *f.* portion, dowry.
aus=weichen, *S.* to give way, retire.
Avignon (Aveenyon), *French city.*

baden, to bathe.

bald, soon, almost; bald ... bald, now ... then.

Band, n. "er, ribbon, band.

bat (bitten). [ton.

Baum, m. "e, tree; =wolle, f. cot-

bedenken, M. to consider, hesitate; n. consideration, hesitation.

Beendigung, f. ending, conclusion.

befallen, S. to befall, attack.

befolgen, to follow, obey.

begeben (sich), S. to go, happen.

begegnen, to meet.

beginnen, S. to begin.

beglücken, to make happy, bless.

behalten, S. to hold, keep.

bei, by, near, with, at one's house.

bei=bringen, M. to enjoin, impress.

Beicht=e, f. confession (religious); =kind, n. penitent.

beide, both, the two, either.

Bein, n. -e, bone; *usually* leg.

beinah'e, almost.

Beispiel, n. -e, example.

bekennen, M. to confess.

beleidigen, to offend, insult.

bemerken, to perceive, remark.

bequemen (sich), to submit.

Beredsamkeit, f. eloquence.

beredt, eloquent.

bereuen, to repent.

berühmt, celebrated, famous.

berühren, to touch.

besagt, aforesaid.

beschämen, to shame.

beschatten, to shade.

beschenken, to present.

beschließen, S. to conclude, resolve.

besinnen (sich), S. to remember.

Besinnung, f. thought, conscious-ness.

besonders, peculiarly, especially.

besser, better.

beständig, constant, continual.

Bestürzung, f. confusion.

beten, to pray.

betrachten, to behold, examine.

betragen (sich), S. to behave.

betrüben, to trouble, grieve.

bevor=stehen, S. to impend, threaten.

beweg=en, to move; S. to induce; –lich, movable, moving; –ung, f. movement, commotion.

beweisen, S. to prove, show.

bewundern, to admire.

bezahlen, to pay, pay for.

biegen, S. to bend, bow.

bieten, S. to bid, offer.

Bild, n. image, picture.

bis, to, till; *with prep.* — an, — auf, —zu, up to, until; — dahin, till then, so far; =her, hitherto.

bitten, S. to beg, ask.

bitterlich, bitterly.

blaß, pale.

bleiben, S. to stay, remain, stop.

Blick, m. look.

blicken, to look.

blitzen, to flash, lighten.

bloß, bare, naked, mere.

blühen, to bloom, flourish.

Blume, f. flower; –n=kelch, m. calyx; –n=spender, m. giver of flowers; –n=strauß, m. "e, nosegay.

Blut, *n.* blood; =**rot,** blood-red.

Blüte, *f.* bloom, blossom.

Boden, *m,* –, bottom, ground, floor.

bog (biegen).

böse, bad, wicked, angry; **der Böse,** the Evil One, the devil.

Bösewicht, *m.* –er, wretch, criminal.

boshaft, wicked, malicious.

Bosheit, *f.* wickedness, malice.

brach (brechen). **brachte** (bringen).

Braut, *f.* (ˮe), bride (betrothed); =**leute,** *pl.;* =**paar,** *n.* bridal pair.

Bräutigam, *m.* betrothed suitor.

brechen, *S.* to break.

brennen, *M.* to burn; *as adj.* **brennend,** burning, bright.

bringen, *M.* to bring.

Bruder, *m.* ˮ, brother.

Brunnen, *m.* –, spring, well.

Brust, *f.* ˮe, breast.

brüten, to brood.

Busch, *m.* ˮe, bush.

Busen, *m.* –, bosom.

Cannes (*French*), Cannes (*town*).

Chronik, *f.* chronicle, annals.

da, *adv.* there, then; *conj.* as, since, when; =**bei,** therewith, also.

dachte (denken).

da-für, for that, instead; on the other hand; =**hin,** thither, hence, away, along; =**hinter,** behind that (it); =**mit,** *adv.* therewith, thereby; *conj.* in order that, that; =**neben,** near (by) it, besides.

dann, then.

dar-an, thereon, at, on, to that, *etc.;* =**auf,** thereupon, on, to, after that, *etc.;* =**aus,** out of, from that, thence.

dar-bieten, *S.* to offer.

dar-ein, into that (it), *etc.*

darf (dürfen).

dar-in, =**innen,** in that, (it), *etc.;* =**über,** over, upon, above, beyond that (it), *etc.,* besides; =**um,** around, about, for that (it), *etc.,* therefore.

daß, that, so that.

da-stehen, *S.* to stand, be there.

da-von, from, of that (it), *etc.;* off, away; some; =**zu,** for, to that (it), *etc.,* besides; =**zwischen,** between, in the midst.

Deckel, *m.* cover, lid.

denken, *M.* to think.

denkwürdig, memorable.

denn, for, then.

deren (der, *dem. or rel.*).

dergleichen (*comp. gen. pl.*), (of) the like, such.

der-, die-, das-selbe, the same, he, she. it.

dessen (der, *dem. or rel.*).

desto, by so much, the (*comp.*).

Diener, *m.* servant, official.

dies-er, –e, –es, this, the latter. =**mal,** this time.

Ding, *n.* –e, thing.

doch, though, yet, surely, after all, pray.

donnern, to thunder, roar.

dort, there, yonder.

drängen, to press, throng.

draußen, without, outside, out of doors.

drehen, to turn.

dreihundert, three hundred.

dringen, *S.* to press, penetrate, urge.

dritt, third.

drüber = darüber.

drum = darum.

dulden, to suffer, bear.

dumm, stupid, dull.

dunkel, dark, obscure.

durch, through, by.

durchlaufen, *S.* to run through, traverse.

durchlöchern, to pierce, break.

durchscheinend, transparent.

dürfen, *M. irr.* to need, dare, may, can.

düster, dark, gloomy.

eben, even, level; *adv.* even, just, exactly; =so, just (as).

eh(e), before; eher, sooner, rather.

Ehe, *f.* marriage; =paar, *n.* bridal pair.   [able.

ehrbar, honorable, honest, vener-

Ehr-e, *f.* honor; =furcht, *f.* reverence, awe; =würdig, venerable, reverend.

eigen, own, peculiar.

eigentlich, proper; *usually adv.*

Eigentum, *n.* property, peculiarity.

eilen, to hasten.

eilfertig, eilig, hasty.

einan'der, one another, each other.

Einbildung, *f.* imagination, fancy.

ein=dringen, *S.* to press into, pierce, enter.

einfältig, simple, silly.

ein=hüllen, to wrap, veil (in).

einig, one, only, united.

einige, *pl. indef.* some, any, a few.

ein=laden, *S.* to invite.

ein'mal, once, one time; auf —, all at once, suddenly; einmal', once on a time, sometime, only; nicht —, not even.

ein=schärfen, to impress, enjoin.

ein=schlafen, *S.* to fall asleep.

ein=sehen, *S.* to see, perceive.

Einwohner, *m.* inhabitant; =schaft, *f.* inhabitants, population.

ein=ziehen, *S.* to move into, enter.

einzig, single, alone, only.

elend, wretched, poor; *noun, n.* wretchedness, misery.

Elefant', *m.* elephant.

empfangen, *S.* to receive.

empor', up, upwards; =heben, *S.* to lift up, raise.

Ende, *n.* -s, -n, end.

endlich, final; *adv.* at last.

Engel, *m.* angel. *eng=narrow*

entdeck-en, to discover, disclose; -ung, *f.* discovery, disclosure.

entfernen, to remove; sich —, to retire, withdraw.

entgegen, towards; =eilen, to hasten to meet; =treten, *S.* to meet.

entgegnen, to reply.

entlarven, to unmask.

entschuldigen, to excuse.

Entsetzen, *n.* horror, terror, shock.

entweder, either.

entzück-en, to enrapture, charm; **-ung,** *f.* rapture, delight.

erbarmen, to move to pity; *noun, n.* pity.

erbau-en, to build up, edify; **-lich,** edifying; **-ung,** *f.* building, foundation, edification.

Erbschaft, *f.* inheritance, legacy.

Erde, *f.* earth.

erfahren, *S.* to learn, experience; *part. adj.* **erfahren,** expert, skilled.

erhalten, *S.* to receive, obtain, keep.

erhellen, to light, make clear; *intr.* to be clear, appear. [hance.

erhöhen, to heighten, raise, en-

erholen, to collect, recover.

erkennen, *M.* to recognize.

erklären, to explain, declare.

erlauben, to allow, permit.

erlauern, to discover (by watching).

erlauschen, to detect (by listening).

Ernst, *m.* earnestness, earnest; *adj. or* **-haft,** earnest, serious.

Eroberung, *f.* conquest, prize.

Erörterung, *f.* discussion, investigation.

erraten, *S.* to guess.

erschaffen, *S.* to create.

erscheinen, *S.* to appear.

erschrak (erschrecken).

erschrecken, to frighten; *intr. S.* to be frightened, start.

erst, first; *adv.* first, at first, only, just.

erstaunen, to be astonished; *noun, n.* astonishment.

ertappen, to catch.

erwachen, to awake.

erzähl-en, to relate, tell (stories); **-ung,** *f.* tale, story, narration.

Erzbösewicht, *m.* **-er,** archvillain.

erzeugen, to beget, produce.

es, it, there, so; *often not trans.*

etwas, something, anything; *adv.* somewhat; **so —,** such a thing.

Eva, Eve.

ewig, eternal, everlasting; **-grün,** evergreen; **-keit,** *f.* eternity.

fahren, *S.* to go, move, start.

Fall, *m.* **ᵘe,** fall, case, event.

falsch, false; **-heit,** *f.* falsehood.

falten, to fold.

Familie, *f.* family.

fand (finden).

fangen, *S.* to catch, seize.

Farbe, *f.* color.

fassen, to seize, hold, contain.

Fassung, *f.* composure.

fast, almost.

Fee, *f.* fairy.

fehlen, to fail, miss, err.

Fehler, *m.* fault, defect.

feierlich, solemn; **-keit,** solemnity, ceremony.

feiern, to solemnise, celebrate.

fein, fine, nice, sly.

Feindschaft, *f.* enmity. [flower.

Feld, *n.* field; **-blume,** *f.* wild

Fels, Felsen, *m.* rock; **-stück,** *n.* **-e,** rock, stone, boulder.

Fenster, *n.* window; **-lein,** *n. dim.*

Ferne, *f.* distance.

Ferse, *f.* heel.

fest, fast, firm, solid.

feurig, fiery, ardent, red.

finden, *S.* to find.

fing (fangen).

Finger, *m.* finger.

finster, dark, gloomy.

Fisch, *m.* fish.

flach, flat.

flattern, to flutter, flit.

Flecken, *m.* village.

flehen, to beseech, implore.

fliegen, *S.* to fly, flutter.

fliehen, *S.* to flee, flee from, avoid.

flog (fliegen).

floh (fliehen).

flüchtig, fugitive, flying, fleeting.

flüstern, to whisper.

folgen, to follow.

folgend, following; **-er=gestalt,** as follows.

folglich, consequently.

foltern, to torture, torment.

fort, forth, on, away, gone; **=fahren,** *S.* to continue.

fragen, to ask.

Frau, *f.* woman, wife, Mrs.

freilich, certainly, indeed.

Fremdling, *m.* foreigner, stranger.

freudig, joyful, glad.

freuen (sich), to rejoice, be glad.

Freund, *m.* **-in,** *f.* friend; **-lich,** friendly, kind.

Frevel, *m.* crime, wrong.

Frevler, *m.* criminal.

Friede(n), *m.* peace.

frisch, fresh, new, cool, lively.

froh, fröhlich, cheerful, happy, glad.

fromm, pious, good, gentle.

früh, early.

Früh(e), *f.* early morning.

füg-en, to fix, arrange; **sich —,** to suit, submit; **–ung,** *f.* arrangement, dispensation.

fuhr (fahren).

führen, to lead, conduct, escort.

füllen, to fill.

fünfzig, funfzig, fifty.

funkeln, to sparkle, glitter.

für, for, instead of.

Furcht, *f.* fear.

fürchten, to fear; **sich —,** to be afraid.

furchtsam, fearful, timid.

Fuß, *m.* "ße, foot, footing.

gab (geben).

Gabe, *f.* gift.

galt (gelten).

Gang, *m.* "e, gait, walk, way.

ganz, whole, entire, all; *adv.* quite.

gar, *adv.* quite, very; **— nicht,** not at all.

geb-en, *S.* to give; **es giebt** (gab), there is, are, was, *etc.*; **=er,** *m.* giver.

geblieben (bleiben).

gebracht (bringen).

gebrochen (brechen).

Geburt, *f.* birth; **-s-ort,** *m.* birthplace.

Gedächtnis, *n.* memory.

Gedanke, *m.* thought.

gedenken, *S.* to remember, mention.

gedrungen (dringen).

Gefahr, *f.* danger, risk.

gefallen, *S.* to please.

gefällig, pleasing, kind.

gefangen (fangen), *adj. or noun,* captive, prisoner.

Geflüster, *n.* whispering.

gefunden (finden).

gegangen (gehen).

gegen, towards, against, about.

Geheimnis, *n.* secret, mystery; **–voll,** secret, mysterious.

gehen, *S.* to go, walk, fare.

gehoben (heben).

gehorchen, to obey.

gehörig, belonging to, proper, due.

gehorsam, obedient; *noun, m.* obedience.

Geier, *m.* vulture, kite.

Geläut(e), *n.* peal (of bells), chime.

Geld, *n.* money.

geliebt, *part. adj. or noun,* beloved.

gelingen, *S. impers.* to succeed.

gelt, well! surely! is it not so?

gelten, *S.* to be worth, be; **gleich —,** to be equal, all the same.

gelungen (gelingen).

gelüsten, to desire, long; *impers.* es gelüstet mir, I long.

Gemüt, *n.* –er, mind, feeling, disposition.

gen = gegen.

genau, exact, accurate.

genommen (nehmen).

genug', enough, sufficient.

geraten, *S.* to fall, get, succeed.

gerecht, right, just.

Gericht, *n.* court, trial, judgment.

geriet (geraten).

gern(e), gladly, willingly; ich sehe gern, I love to see, am fond of.

Geschäft, *n.* business, affair, job.

geschah (geschehen).

geschehen, *S.* to happen, occur, be done.

Geschenk, *n.* gift, present.

Geschichte, *f.* history, story.

geschienen (scheinen).

geschlichen (schleichen).

geschlungen (schlingen).

Geschrei, *n.* cry, outcry.

geschrieben (schreiben).

geschwind, swift, quick.

geschwunden (schwinden).

Gesellschaft, *f.* company, society.

Gesicht, *n.* –er, face.

Gespiel–e, *m.,* **–in,** *f.* playmate.

Gespräch, *n.* conversation.

gesprächig, affable, talkative.

gesprochen (sprechen).

Gestalt, *f.* form, figure, shape.

gestehen, *S.* to confess.

gestern, yesterday.

gesund, sound, healthy.

gethan (thun).

Getöse, *n.* noise.

getrieben (treiben).

Gewalt, *f.* force, power, violence.

gewiesen (weisen).

gewinnen, *S.* to win, gain, get.

gewiß, certain, sure.

Gewissen, *n.* conscience.

gewöhnen, to accustom, use.

gewohnt, accustomed, usual.

Gewölbe, *n.* vault, arch, booth.

gewunden (winden).

gezogen (ziehen).

gieb–ſt–t (geben).

ging (gehen).

Glaube(n), *m.* –ns,–n, belief, faith.

glauben, to believe.

gleich, like, equal, same; *adv.* alike, equally, immediately; =gültig, equivalent, indifferent.

Glied, *n.* limb, member.

Glocke, *f.* bell.

Glück, *n.* happiness, (good) luck; –lich, happy, fortunate.

glühen, to glow, burn.

Glut, *f.* glow, heat.

gnädig, gracious, kind, merciful.

Gold, *n.* gold; =grün, golden-green.

gottlos, godless, impious.

Graf, *m.* –en, count.

Gräfin, *f.* countess.

Granat'buſch, *m.* pomegranate bush.

Gras, *n.* grass.

Graſſe (*French*), Grass*e* (*town*).

grau, gray, hoary.

grauſam, cruel; –keit, *f.* cruelty.

grauſenhaft, horrible.   [man.

greis, gray, hoary; *noun, m.* old

Grenze, *f.* limit, frontier.

Griechenland, *n.* Greece.

Grimm, *m.* anger, malice.

groß, größer, größt, great, large, tall.

grün, green.

Grund, *m.* ˮe, ground, bottom, reason; =ſatz, *m.* principle, habit.

Gruß, *m.* ˮße, greeting, salute.

grüßen, to greet, salute.

Gunſt, *f.* ˮe, favor, kindness.

gut, beſſer, beſt, good; *adv.* well.

Gut, *n.* property, farm; ˮchen, *n. dim.*

gütig, good, kind.

Gutsbeſitzer, *m.* landowner.

Hader, *m.* quarrel.

hadern, to quarrel.

halb, half.

Hälfte, *f.* half.

Hals, *m.* ˮe, neck.

halten, *S.* to hold, keep, stop, deem; — für, to hold for, esteem.

Hand, *f.* ˮe, hand.

Handel, *m.* ˮ, affair, business.

Hand=habe, *f.* handle; =kuß, *m.* hand kiss; =ſchrift, *f.* hand-writing, manuscript.

hangen, hängen, *S.* to hang.

harmlos, harmless, innocent.

Harniſch, *m.* armor, arms.

hart, ˮ, hard; =herzig, hard-hearted; –keit, *f.* –ness; =hörig, hard of hearing, deaf; –keit, *f.* –ness.

haſſen, to hate.

Haupt, *n.* head, chief.

Haus, *n.* house; nach, zu, von Hauſe, home, at, from, home.

heben, *S.* to lift, raise.

heilig, holy, sacred, saint; *as noun*, saint; –tum, *n.* holy thing, relic, sanctuary.

heim, home; =kehr, *f.* return home; =weg, *m.* way home.

heimlich, secret; –keit, *f.* secrecy.

heimtückisch, mischievous, malicious.

heißen, *S.* to bid, call, be called, be said, mean.

her, hither, here, along, ago.

herab, down; **=hängen,** *S.* to hang down; **=lassen (sich),** *S.* to condescend.

herbei, hither, on, up (hither); **=holen,** to fetch, bring; **=rufen,** *S.* to call up.

Herr, *m.* -n, -en, master, lord, gentlemen, sir, Mr.

Herz, *n.* -ens, -en, heart; **=haft,** bold, courageous; **=lich,** heartily, cordial; *adv.* heartily, utterly.

heulen, to howl, roar.

heut–e, to-day, now (a days); **=ig,** of to-day, modern.

hielt (halten).

hier, here.

hieß (heißen).

Himmel, *m.* heaven, sky.

hin, thither, hence, away, along, gone.

hinab, down; **=sinken,** *S.* to sink down.

hinauf, up, upwards.

hinaus, out, away; **=laufen,** *S.* to run out; **=weisen,** *S.* to order out; **=werfen,** *S.* to throw out, put out.

hinein, into, in.

hing (hangen).

hingegen, on the contrary, whereas.

hin=gehen, *S.* to go (away, along, off), pass; **=nehmen,** *S.* to take (away, along, off).

hinter, behind, back; **=grund,** *m.* background.

hinunter, down, downwards.

hoch, höher, höchst, high.

Hochzeit, *f.* wedding; **–s=tag,** *m.* — day.

hoffen, to hope.

Hoffnung, *f.* hope.

hoh– (hoch).

Hoheit, *f.* height, dignity.

hold, gentle, kind, sweet.

Homer', *m.* Homer.

horchen, to listen.

hören, to hear.

hübsch, pretty.

hundert, (a) hundred.

hüpfen, to hop, skip, leap.

Hut, *m.* "e, hat.

Hütte, *f.* hut, cottage.

ihr, Ihr, you; **ihr,** to her, her, their.

ihrer, hers, of her; theirs, of them.

im = in dem.

immer, always, ever; **auf —,** forever; **=dar = immer.**

in, in, into.

indem, meanwhile; *conj.* while, as.

indeß, indessen, meanwhile, however; *conj.,* while, as, though.

inner, inner, internal.

Insel, *f.* island.

inzwisch'en, meanwhile; *conj.,* while.

ja, yes, indeed, surely, you know.

Jacques (*French*), *m.* James.

Jahr, *n.* -e, year; **=markt,** *m.* fair.

Jammer, *m.* sorrow, grief, pity.

Jawort, *n.* consent.

je, ever.

jeder, each, every, any; =mann, everyone, anybody.

jedoch, however, nevertheless.

jeher (von), from the first, always.

jetzt, now; **jetzig,** present.

jung, ", young.

Junge, *m.* youngster, youth.

Jungfrau, *f.* virgin, young lady, miss.

Jüngling, *m.* youth, young man.

kam (kommen).

Kammer, *f.* chamber, room; **Kämmerlein,** *n. dim.*

kann (können).

kannte (kennen).

Kasse, *f.* treasury, money-box.

kauf–en, to buy; =mann, *m.* merchant.

kaum, hardly, scarcely.

kein, no, not any; –er, no one, none.

kennen, *M.* to know; — lernen, to become acquainted with.

Kiesel, *m.* flint; =hart, flinty.

Kind, *n.* child; –lein, *n. dim.*

Kirch–e, *f.* church; =zehnt(e), *m.* church tithe.

Klage, *f.* complaint, accusation.

kleiden, to clothe, dress.

klein, little, small; =asien, *n.* Asia Minor.

Kleinigkeit, *f.* trifle.

Knecht, *m.* servant.

Knoten, *m.* –, knot.

knüpfen, to tie.

kommen, *S.* to come.

König, *m.* king; –in, *f.* queen.

können, *M. irr.,* to be able, can, may.

Kopf, *m.* "e, head.

Korb, *m.* "e, basket; *fig.* refusal.

kostbar, costly, fine.

kosten, to cost; to taste.

köstlich, costly, precious, delicious.

kränken, to grieve, offend.

Kranz, *m.* "e, garland, wreath; "chen, "lein, *n. dim.*

Kraut, *n.* herb, weed.

Kreide, *f.* chalk.

Krug, *m.* "e, pitcher, vase, jar.

kühl, cool.

Kummer, *m.* grief, sorrow.

künftig, future; *adv.* in future.

Kuß, *m.* "sse, kiss.

küssen, to kiss.

lachen, to laugh, smile.

lächeln, to smile.

lag (liegen).

Lager, *n.* bed.

Lamm, *n.* lamb; "lein, *n. dim.*

La Napoule, *(French town);* –er, *m.,* –erin, *f.* –ese, *m.* inhabitant of —.

Land, *n.* land, country; =vogt, *m.* local judge, prefect.

ländlich, rural, rustic, local.

lang, ", long, tall; *adv.* lang(e), long (time).

langsam, slow, tedious.

las (lesen).

lassen, *S.* to leave, let, cause, have (done).

lauern, to lurk, watch.

laufen, *S.* to run.

laure, (lauern).

lauschen, to listen (secretly).

laut, loud, aloud.

leben, to live; *noun, n.* life.

lebendig, living, alive.

leer, empty, mere.

legen, to lay, put.

Lehre, *f.* doctrine, lesson, lecture.

Leib, *m.* −er, body.

leicht, light, easy.

Leid, *n.* harm, pain, sorrow; **es ist** (thut) **mir leid,** I am sorry.

leise, low, soft (voice).

leisten, to perform, afford, give.

lernen, to learn.

lesen, *S.* to read.

letzt, last.

leugnen, to deny.

Leute, *pl.* people, folk.

Licht, *n.* light, candle.

lieb, dear; **— gewinnen,** to fall in love with; **— haben,** to love.

Liebe, *f.* love.

lieben, to love; **−s-würdig,** lovely.

lieber, *adv. comp.* sooner, rather.

Liebhaber, *m.* lover.

lieblich, lovely, dear, sweet.

Lied, *n.* song.

lief (laufen).

liegen, *S.* to lie, lie down.

ließ (lassen).   [left.

link, left; *adv.* **links,** on, to the

Lippe, *f.* lip.

lispeln, to lisp, murmur.

Livre (*French*) *m.* franc (*coin*).

los, loose, free; **−knüpfen,** to untie.

lösen, to loose, untie, solve.

Lüge, *f.* lie, falsehood.

lüstern, longing, eager.

Lust, *f.* ″e, pleasure, desire, wish; **−wandeln,** to walk, stroll.

machen, to make, do, matter.

mächtig, mighty, powerful, capable.

Mädchen, *n.* girl, maiden.

mag (mögen).

Mahl, *n.* meal.

malen, to paint.

man, one, anyone, we, they, *etc., or passive.*

manch, many, many a; **−erlei,** of many kinds, divers.

Mann, *m.* ″er, man, husband.

Markt, *m.* ″e, market; **−tag,** *m.* — day.

Maus, *f.* ″e, mouse.

Meer, *n.* −e, sea; **−busen,** *m.* bay.

mehr, more.

mein−en, to think, mean, say; **−ung,** *f.* opinion, meaning.

meist, most.

Mensch, *m.* −en, man, person; **−lich,** human, humane.

merkwürdig, remarkable.

Mieder, *n.* bodice.

mischen, to mix, mingle.

Mißverständnis, *n.* misunderstanding.

mit, with; *adv.* together, also, too.

Mitleib(en), *n.* pity; **-ig**, pitiful, compassionate.

Mitte, *f.* middle, midst.

mitten in, in the midst of.

mochte, möchte (mögen).

mögen, *M. irr.* to like, may, can.

Montag, *m.* Monday.

Morgen, *m.* morning; **des —s**, in the morning; **-rot**, *n.* dawn; *adv.* **morgen**, to-morrow.

morsch, rotten, brittle.

Mühe, *f.* pains, trouble.

Mund, *m.* **"e(r)**, mouth.

müssen, *M. irr.* to be compelled, must.

Mut, *m.* mood, spirit, courage.

Mutter, *f.* **"**, mother.

Myrte, *f.* myrtle.

nach, towards, to, according to, after; **— und —**, by degrees.

Nachbar, *m.* **-s**, **-n**; **-in**, *f.* neighbor.

nach-schreien, *S.* to cry after.

Nacht, *f.* **"e**, night.

nah(e), (näher, nächst), near.

Nähe, *f.* nearness, neighborhood.

nahm (nehmen).

Name, *m.* **-ns**, **-n**, name.

nämlich, same; *adv.* namely, especially.

nannte (nennen).

Napoule, *see* La Napoule.

Näscherei, *f.* dainty, tidbit.

Nase, *f.* nose; **-n-spitze**, tip of the nose.

naß, **"**, wet, damp.

natürlich, natural; *adv.* of course.

neben, nebst, near by, with.

necken, to tease.

nehmen, *S.* to take, seize.

nein, no.

nennen, *M.* to name, call.

neu, new, late; **-gier(de)**, *f.* curiosity; **-gierig**, curious; **-vermählt**, newly married.

neunt, ninth.

nicht, not.

nichts, nothing.

nicken, to nod, beckon.

nie, never; **-mals**, never.

nieder, down.

nieder-schlagen, *S.* to cast down, refute; **-geschlagen**, *part. adj.* cast down, depressed.

niedlich, neat, pretty.

nimm, -st, -t (nehmen).

noch, still, yet, even; *conj.* nor.

Not, *f.* **"e**, necessity, need, distress.

nun, now, well; *conj.* as, since.

nur, only, but, just; **— nicht**, not even.

ob, whether, if; **— gleich, — wohl**, although (*or in one word*).

obrigkeitlich, official.

obwohl, although (*or sep.*).

oder, or.

öffentlich, public, open.

öffnen, to open.

oft, öfters, often.

ohne, without; **ohne ... zu, ohne daß**, without **-ing**; **-dem**, besides; **-hin**, besides, anyhow.

Ohr, *n.* -es, -en, ear.

Öl, *n.* oil; =baum, *m.* olive tree; =garten, *m.* olive orchard.

Orange, *f.* orange.

ordn-en, to order, arrange; —ung, *f.* order, arrangement, manner.

Ort, *m.* -e *or* ¨er, place.

Paar, *n.* pair; ein paar, a few.

Pächter, *m.* tenant, renter.

Palme, *f.* palm (tree).

Papier', *n.* paper; =streif(en), *m.* strip of paper.

Paradies', *n.* paradise.

passen, to pass, fit, suit; — auf, to apply to.

Pa'ter (*Latin*) *m.* father, priest.

Pein, *f.* pain, torment.

Perle, *f.* pearl.

Person', *f.* person.

Pfand, *n.* pledge, pawn.

Pfarr-er, *m.* parson; =haus, *n.* parsonage.

pflegen, *rarely S.* to be accustomed, Pflicht, *f.* duty.   [use.

Pharao, *m.* Pharaoh.

Pierre (*French*) *m.* Peter.

Plan, *m.* -e, *or* ¨e, plan.

plaudern, to chat, talk.

Pomeranze, *f.* orange, orange tree.

Porzellan', *n.* porcelain.

Pracht, *f.* splendor, beauty.

prächtig, splendid, beautiful.

predigen, to preach.

Probe, *f.* proof, trial, specimen.

Protokoll', *n.* record, minutes.

Proven'ce (*French*) *f.* Provence.

Rache, *f.* revenge, vengeance.

Rand, *m.* ¨er, edge, border, rim.

raten, *S.* to advise; to guess.

Ratte, *f.* rat.

rauschen, to rustle.

rechn-en, to reckon, count; —ung, *f.* reckoning, account.

recht, right, just; *adv.* right, quite, very; recht haben, to be right.

Recht, *n.* right, law, justice.

rechtlich, lawful, honest, righteous.

rechts, on *or* to the right (hand).

reden, to speak, talk.

redlich, honest, candid.

regen, to move, stir.

reich, rich.

reichen, to reach, attain.

Reichtum, *m.* -tümer, riches, wealth.

Reihe, *f.* row, rank; der — nach, in succession.

Reise, *f.* journey.

reisen, to travel, go.

reißen, *S.* to tear.

reiten, *S.* to ride.

reizen, to excite, provoke, charm.

reizend, *part. adj.* charming.

Religion', *f.* religion.

rennen, *M.* to run.

retten, to save, rescue; sich —, to escape, flee.

Reue, *f.* repentance, penitence.

reuen, to repent, make repent; es reuet mich, I repent.

Richter, *m.* judge.

richterlich, judicial.

riechen, *S.* to smell.

rief (rufen).

riet (raten).

Ring, *m.* ring.

riß (reißen).

ritt (reiten),

roch (riechen).

Rock, *m.* ᵉ, coat, gown.

Rose, *f.* rose; **–n-knospe**, *f.* rosebud; **=kranz**, *m.* wreath of roses, rosary.

rot, , red; *noun, n.* red, redness.

rufen, *S.* to call, cry out, exclaim.

ruhen, to rest.

ruhig, quiet, calm.

rühren, to move, touch.

rührend, *part. adj.* moving, touching.

rüsten, to prepare, arm.

's (es, *rarely* das).

Sache, *f.* thing, affair.

sagen, to say, tell.

sah (sehen).

sammeln, to collect, gather.

sam(m)t, with, together with.

sang (singen).

sank (sinken).

sann (sinnen).

satt, satisfied, full; **sich — sehen**, to see *or* look enough.

sättigen, to satisfy.

Satz, *m.* ᵉ, sentence, text.

Schachtel, *f.* box.

Schade(n), *m.* , damage, hurt, pity; **=froh**, mischievous, malicious. [work.

schaffen, *S.* to create; *W.* to do,

Schalkheit, *f.* roguishness, mischief.

schämen (sich), to be ashamed.

Schatten, *m.* –, shade, shadow.

Schau, *f.* show, view; **zur —**, openly, for show.

schauen, to look, view.

scheinen, *S.* to shine, seem, appear.

schelmisch, roguish.

Scherbe, *f.* fragment, piece.

Scherge, *m.* constable, beadle.

scherzen, to jest, joke.

schicken, to send.

schien (scheinen).

Schlaf, *m.* sleep; **=kammer**, *f.* bedroom.

schlafen, *S.* to sleep.

Schläfer, *m.* sleeper.

schlagen, *S.* to beat, strike, throw.

schlang (schlingen).

Schlange, *f.* snake, serpent.

schlank, slender, slim.

schlau, sly, sharp.

schleichen, *S.* to creep, glide.

schleudern, to fling, hurl.

schlief (schlafen).

schließen, *S.* to shut, close, lock, join.

schlimm, bad.

schlingen, *S.* to twine, wind, wrap.

Schloß, *n.* castle; **=trümmer**, *pl.* — ruins.

schloß (schließen).

schluchzen, to sob.

schlug (schlagen).

schlucken, to swallow.

Schlummer, *m.* slumber, sleep.

Schmach, *f.* insult, shame.

schnäbeln (sich), to bill, kiss.

Schnee, *m.* snow; =weiß, snow-white.

schnell, quick, swift.

Schnur, *f.* -en, *or* ⁿe, string, cord.

schon, already, surely, even.

schön, beautiful, handsome, fine; -heit, *f.* beauty.

Schreck, *m.* terror, fright.

schreib-en, *S.* to write; -er, *m.* writer, clerk.

schreien, *S.* to cry, scream.

schrie (schreien).

Schritt, *m.* step.

schüchtern, timid.

Schuld, *f.* debt, fault; schuld sein an, to be to blame for; -ig, indebted, guilty, culpable.

schütteln, to shake.

Schutz, *m.* protection, defence; =redner, *m.* advocate, defender.

schützen, to protect, defend.

schwanken, to wave, waver.

Schwanz, *m.* ⁿe, tail, train.

schweben, to hover, soar, glide.

schweigen, *S.* to be silent, hush.

schwenken, to wave, rinse.

schwieg (schweigen).

Schwiegersohn, *m.* son-in-law.

Schwindel, *m.* giddiness, vertigo.

schwinden, *S.* to vanish.

schwor (schwören).

schwören, *S.* to swear, vow.

Seele, *f.* soul; -n=voll, soulful, feeling.

Segen, *m.* blessing.

sehen, *S.* to see, look.

sehr, very, much, very much.

seiden, silken, of silk. [sake.

seinetwillen, on his account, for his

seit, since; =dem, since.

seitwärts, sideways, aside.

selbst, self; *adv.* even.

selig, happy, blessed.

senken, to sink, lower.

setzen, to set, put, appoint; sich —, to sit down.

seufz-en, to sigh; -er, *m.* sigh.

sieben, seven; sieb(en)zig, seventy.

siegreich, victorious.

sieh(e), -st, -t (sehen).

singen, *S.* to sing.

sinken, *S.* to sink, fall.

sinnen, *S.* to think, reflect.

sittsam, modest; -keit, *f.* modesty.

sitzen, *S.* to sit.

so, so, thus, as, yet; =bald, as soon as; =gar, even, actually.

solch (-er, -e, -es), such.

sollen, *irr.* to be obliged, shall, be said.

Sommer, *m.* summer; =nacht, *f.* — night.

sondern, but.

Sonne, *f.* sun.

Sonntag, *m.* Sunday.

sonntäglich, of Sunday, festive.

sonst, otherwise, else, formerly, usually.

sorgen, to care.

Sou(s), *m.* sous, cent (*French*).

sparen, to spare, save.

spät, late. [*m.* giver.

spend-en, to dispense, give; -er,

Spiel, *n.* -e, game, play.
spielen, to play.
sprach (sprechen).
Sprache, *f.* speech, language.
sprang (springen).
sprechen, *S.* to speak, say.
springen, *S.* to spring, leap, break.
Spruch, *m.* "e, saying, sentence.
Stadt, *f.* "e, city, town.
stammeln, to stammer.
stand (stehen).
stecken, to stick, put, hide.
stehen, *S.* to stand; — bleiben, to stop.
steigen, *S.* to step (up), rise, mount.
Stein, *m.* stone.
Stelle, *f.* place, spot.
stellen, to place, put.
Stengel, *m.* stem, stalk.
stieg (steigen).
stiften, to found, cause, effect.
still(e), still, quiet, silent.
Stille, *f.* stillness, quiet, silence.
Stimme, *f.* voice, vote.
Stirn(e), *f.* forehead, brow.
stolz, proud; *noun, m.* pride.
Strafe, *f.* punishment, penalty.
strafen, to punish.
strahlen, to beam, shine.
Straße, *f.* street, road.
sträuben (sich), to resist, refuse.
Strauß, *m.* "e, bunch (of flowers), nosegay.
Streich, *m.* stroke, trick.
streichen, *S.* to stroke, touch, pass over.
Streif(en), *m.* strip.

streifen, to touch, graze.
Streit, *m.* quarrel, contest.
streuen, to strew, scatter.
strich (streichen).
Stück, *n.* -e, piece, bit; –chen, *n. dim.* little bit, trick.
stumm, dumb, mute.
Stunde, *f.* hour; "chen, "lein, *n. dim.*
stürzen, to fall, rush, plunge.
suchen, to seek.
Sünde, *f.* sin; –n-fall, *m.* the fall of man (by sin).
sündigen, to sin.
süß, sweet.

Tag, *m.* -e, day.
Tanz, *m.* "e, dance.
tanzen, to dance.
Taub-e, *f.* dove, pigeon; "chen, *n. dim.*
Tauf-e, *f.* baptism; =handlung, *f.* act of baptism; =kind, *n.* child by baptism.
tausend, (a) thousand.
teuer, dear.
Teufel, *m.* devil.
That, *f.* deed, act.
that (thun).
Thor, *m.* -en, Thörin, *f.* fool.
Thrän-e, *f.* tear; –chen, *n. dim.*
thun, *irr.* to do, make.
Thüre, *f.* door.
tief, deep.
Tiger, *m.* tiger.
Tisch, *m.* table.
Tochter, *f.* ", daughter.

Tod, *m.* death; **-es-verdruß,** *m.* deadly vexation.

Trabant', *m.* guard, satellite.

tragen, *S.* to bear, carry, wear.

trat (treten).

Traube, *f.* bunch of grapes, grape.

trauen, to trust; to marry.

träumen, to dream.

traurig, sad, sorrowful.

Trauung, *f.* marriage.

treiben, *S.* to drive, push, carry on.

Trennung, *f.* separation.

treten, *S.* to tread, step.

Treue, *f.* truth, fidelity.

trieb (treiben).

trinken *S.* to drink.

Trinkgeld, *n.* drink money, tip.

trippeln, to trip.

Tritt, *m.* step, footstep.

triumphie'ren, to triumph.

trug (tragen).

Trümmer, *pl.* ruins, fragments.

Tück-e, *f.* trick; **-isch,** tricky, knavish.

Tugend, *f.* virtue.

übel, evil, ill, bad; *as noun, n.*

übelan, *see* übel.

üben, to practice, exercise.

über, over, above, beyond, on, about, during, *etc.;* **-all,** everywhere.

Überbringer, *m.* bearer, messenger.

übereilen, to hurry (overmuch).

über-gehen, *S.* to go over, pass over, change; **übergehen,** *S.* to pass over, transgress, omit.

überreichen, to hand over, deliver.

überrumpeln, to take by surprise.

Ufer, *n.* shore.

um, around, about, for, after; **— so,** by so much; **— zu** (*w. infin.*), in order to.

um-drehen, to turn round.

umsäuseln, to hover (wave) around.

um-sehen (sich), *S.* to look around.

unbefangen, frank, ingenuous.

unbemittelt, without means, portionless.

unbeschädigt, uninjured, safe.

unbesonnen, thoughtless; **-heit,** *f.* thoughtlessness.

unerschöpflich, inexhaustible.

ungefähr, about, nearly, perhaps.

ungerecht, unjust; **-igkeit,** *f.* injustice.

ungestüm, violent, passionate.

Unglück, *n.* misfortune, unhappiness.

unglückselig, unfortunate, unhappy.

Unheil, *n.* mischief, disaster.

unmöglich, impossible.

unrecht, wrong; *noun, n.* wrong, injustice; **— haben,** to be wrong.

Unschuld, *f.* innocence; **-ig,** innocent.

unsichtbar, invisible.

unter, under, beneath, among, between.

unter-gehen, *S.* to go down, sink, set.

Untersuchung, *f.* investigation, examination.

unterweg(e)s, on the way.

unvergleichlich, incomparable.

unverhofft, unhoped, unexpected.
unverletzt, unhurt, safe.
unverschämt, shameless, impudent.
unverzeihlich, unpardonable.
unvorsichtig, imprudent, improvident.
Urteil, *n.* -e, judgment, verdict.

Vater, *m.* ꝰ, father.
Veilchen, *n.* violet; =blau, violet-blue; =farben, violet colored.
verabreden, to agree (upon).
verachten, to despise, contemn.
verächtlich, contemptible, contemptuous.
verbergen, *S.* to hide, conceal.
verborgen (verbergen).
Verbrech-en, *n.* crime; -er, *m.* criminal.
verdächtig, suspicious.
verdenken, *M.* to take amiss, blame.
verderben, *S.* to spoil, ruin, corrupt; *noun, n.* ruin, corruption.
verdrieß-en, *S.* to vex, grieve; -lich, vexatious, vexed.
verdroß, (verdrießen).
Verdruß, *m.* ꝰsse, vexation, offence.
vergaß (vergessen).
vergeben, *S.* to forgive.
vergehen, *S.* to pass (away), cease, elapse.
vergessen, *S.* to forget.
vergolden, to gild.
verhaften, to arrest, imprison.
verirren (sich), to lose one's way, stray, be confused.
verkleiden, to disguise.

verkünd(ig)en, to announce.
verlangen, to desire, ask; *impers.* mich verlangt nach), I long for.
verlassen, *S.* to forsake, abandon; sich — auf, to rely on.
verlieren, *S.* to lose.
verloren (verlieren).
vermähl-en, to marry; -ung, *f.* marriage.
vermutlich, probable.
vernehmen, *S.* to perceive, hear, learn.
Vernichtung, *f.* annihilation, destruction.
verraten, *S,* to betray.
verschmähen, to disdain, scorn.
verschwinden, *S.* to vanish, disappear.
versehen, *S.* to overlook; to provide; *reflex. w. gen.* to foresee, expect; *noun,* Versehen, *n.* oversight, error.
versöhnen, to reconcile.
versprechen, *S.* to promise.
verständig, intelligent, sensible.
verstecken, to hide, conceal.
verstehen, *S.* to understand; sich — auf, to know well, be expert in.
verstellen, to misrepresent, disguise.
verstocken, to harden.
verteidigen, to defend.
verwirrt, entangled, confused.
verwünsch-en, to curse; -t, *part. adj.* accursed, cursed; -ung, *f.* cursing, curse.
verzehren, to consume.
verzeihen, *S.* to pardon.

Verzweiflung, *f.* despair, desperation.

viel, much; *pl.* many; **—erlei,** of many kinds, various.

vielleicht, perhaps.

vier, four; **—t,** fourth; **=zehn,** fourteen; vierzehn Tage, a fortnight.

Viertel, *n.* fourth, quarter; **=jahr,** *n.* quarter of a year, three months.

Viguerie¹ (*French*) *f.* local court.

voll, full.

vollbringen, *M.* to complete, accomplish, execute.

vollkommen, complete, perfect.

vollziehen, *S.* to execute, perform.

vom = von dem.

von, from, of, by, *etc.*

vor, before (ago), for, with, from, against, *etc.*

voraus, before, in advance, ahead; **— haben,** to have the advantage; **=gehen,** to go ahead, precede.

vorbei, by, past, over.

vor=bringen, *M,* to bring forward, allege.

=fallen, *S.* to occur, happen.

vorher, before, previously.

vorn(e), before, in front.

vorsichtig, prudent, cautious.

vor=stellen, to present, represent.

Vorwurf, *m.* ˮe, reproach.

vor=ziehen, *S.* to prefer.

vorzüglich, preferable, special; *adv.* especially.

Wa(a)re, *see* Ware.

wachen, to watch, be awake.

wachsen, *S.* to grow.

wahr, true.

während, during; *conj.* while.

wahrhaft(ig), true, real, truthful; *adv.* in truth, really.

wahrlich, *adv.* truly, really.

Wald, *m.* ˮer, wood, forest.

wand (winden).

wandte (wenden).

ward (werden).

Ware, *f.* wares, goods.

warf (werfen).

warten, to wait; **— auf,** — for.

warum, why.

was, what, which, that; how, why; *for* etwas, something, anything.

waschen, *S.* to wash.

Wechsel, *m.* change, exchange; **=gesang,** *m.* ˮe, alternate song, "round."

weder, neither.

Weg, *m.* way, road, journey.

wegen, on account of, for sake of.

wehen, to blow, wave.

Weib, *n.* woman, wife; **—chen,** **—er-chen,** *n. dim.;* **—lich,** female, feminine.

weich, soft.

weichen, *S.* to yield.

weigern (sich), to refuse.

weil, because.

Weile, *f.* while, time.

Wein, *m.* wine; **=berg,** *m.;* **=garten,** *m.* vineyard; **=traube,** *f.* bunch of grapes, grape.

weinen, to weep.

weis, weise, wise, knowing.

Weise, *f.* way, manner.

weislich, *adv.* wisely.

weiß, white.

weiß (wissen).

welch, who, which, that, what; some.

Welle, *f.* wave.

Welt, *f.* world.

wenden, *M.* to turn.

wenig, little; *pl.* few; **ein —,** a little.

wenn, when, if; **— auch, — gleich,** although.

wer, who, whoever.

werfen, *S.* to throw, cast, pelt.

Werk, *n.* -e, work.

wert, worth, worthy, precious.

Wesen, *n.* being, nature.

wich (weichen).

wider, against.

widerlich, disagreeable, repulsive.

Widerspruch, *m.* contradiction.

Widerstand, *m.* resistance.

widerstehen, *S.* to resist, oppose.

widerstreben, to strive against, resist.

wie, how, as, as if.

wieder, again, back.

wiederhallen, to resound, re-echo.

wiederholen, to repeat.

wild, wild.

will (wollen).

Wille, *m.* -ns, -n, will; **um — willen,** for the sake of, on account of.

winden, *S.* to wind, twist, wrap.

Wirkung, *f.* action, effect.

wissen, *M. irr.* to know.

Witwe, *f.* widow.

wo, where, when.

Woche, *f.* week.

woher, whence, how.

wohin, whither, where.

wohl, well, surely, indeed, perhaps; *in comp.* well, very; **=thun,** to do well, do good.

wohnen, to dwell, live.

wollen, *irr.* to will, wish, claim.

worden (werden).

wozu, for what, why.

Wunder, *n.* wonder, miracle; **=blume,** *f.* miraculous flower; **=schön,** very beautiful.

wunderbar, wonderful, miraculous.

wunderlich, wonderful, strange, odd.

Wurf, *m.* ⁻e, throw, cast.

wußte (wissen).

Wut, *f.* rage, fury.

wütend, raging, furious.

zagen, to be afraid, tremble.

zahlen, to pay, pay for.

Zank, *m.* ⁻e, quarrel.

zärtlich, tender; **=keit,** *f.* tenderness.

Zauber, *m.* -, charm, magic; **=er,** *m.* magician, conjuror.

zehnt, tenth; *noun,* **Zehnt(e),** *m.* tithe.

zeigen, to show, point out.

Zeit, *f.* time.

zerbrechen, *S.* to break (to pieces).

zerbrochen (zerbrechen).

zerreißen, *S.* to tear up.

zertreten, *S.* to trample, crush.
Zeug–e, *m.* –in, *f.* witness.
zieh (ziehen).
ziehen, *S.* to draw, pull, move.
zierlich, neat, nice, pretty.
Zimmer, *n.* room.
Zitrone, *f.* lemon.
zittern, to tremble.
zog (ziehen).
Zorn, *m.* anger; –ig, angry.
zu, to, at, by, for, on, to one's house;
   adv. too.
=dem, in addition, besides.
zu-flüstern, to whisper to.
zugleich, at once, at the same time.
zu-lispeln, to lisp to.
zuletzt, at last, finally.
zum = zu dem.
zumal, especially.
Zuneigung, *f.* inclination, affection.

zur = zu der.
zu-reden, to exhort, persuade.
zürnen, to be angry.
zurück, back, backwards, behind.
   =gehen, *S.* to go back, return.
zusammen, together.
Zuspruch, *m.* address, exhorta-
   tion.
zu-werfen, *S.* to throw at *or* to.
zwang (zwingen).
zwanzig, twenty.
zwar, indeed, in truth.
zwei, two; =mal, twice.
Zweifel, *m.* doubt.
zweifeln, to doubt.
zweit, second.
Zwietracht, *f.* dissension, discord.
zwingen, *S.* to force, compel.
zwischen, between, among; =ein, in
   between, among, meanwhile.

ADVERTISEMENTS.

Heath's Modern Language Series.

GERMAN GRAMMARS AND READERS.

Nix's Erstes deutsches Schulbuch. For primary classes. Illus. 202 pages. 35 cts.

Joynes-Meissner German Grammar. A *working* Grammar, elementary, yet complete. Half leather. $1.12.

Alternative Exercises. Can be used, for the sake of change, instead of those in the *Joynes-Meissner* itself. 54 pages. 15 cts.

Joynes's Shorter German Grammar. Part I of the above. Half leather. 80 cts.

Harris's German Lessons. Elementary Grammar and Exercises for a short course, or as introductory to advanced grammar. Cloth. 60 cts.

Sheldon's Short German Grammar. For those who want to begin reading as soon as possible, and have had training in some other languages. Cloth. 60 cts.

Babbitt's German at Sight. A syllabus of elementary grammar, with suggestions and practice work for reading at sight. Paper. 10 cts.

Ball's German Drill Book. Companion to any grammar. 80 cts.

Faulhaber's One Year Course in German. 60 cts.

Krüger and Smith's Conversation Book. 40 pages. Cloth. 25 cts.

Meissner's German Conversation. A scheme of rational conversation. 65 cts.

Harris's German Composition. Elementary, progressive, and varied selections, with full notes and vocabulary. Cloth. 50 cts.

Wesselhoeft's Exercises in German Conversation and Composition. 50 cts.

Wesselhoeft's German Composition. With notes and vocabulary. 40 cts.

Hatfield's Materials for German Composition. Based on *Immensee* and on *Höher als die Kirche*. Paper. 33 pages. Each, 12 cts.

Horning's Materials for German Composition. Based on *Der Schwiegersohn*. 32 pages. 12 cts.

Stüven's Praktische Anfangsgründe. A conversational beginning book with vocabulary and grammatical appendix. Cloth. 203 pages. 70 cts.

Foster's Geschichten und Märchen. For young children. 25 cts.

Guerber's Märchen und Erzählungen, I. With vocabulary and questions in German on the text. Cloth. 162 pages. 60 cts.

Guerber's Märchen und Erzählungen, II. With vocabulary. Follows the above or serves as independent reader. Cloth. 202 pages. 65 cts.

Joynes's German Reader. Progressive, both in text and notes, has a complete vocabulary, also English Exercises. Half leather, 90 cts. Cloth, 75 cts.

Deutsch's Colloquial German Reader. Anecdotes, tables of phrases and idioms, and selections in prose and verse, with notes and vocabulary. Cloth. 90 cts.

Boisen's German Prose Reader. Easy and interesting selections of graded prose, with notes, and vocabulary. Cloth. 90 cts.

Huss's German Reader. Easy and slowly progressive selections in prose and verse. With especial attention to cognates. Cloth. 233 pages. 70 cents.

Spanhoofd's Lehrbuch der deutschen Sprache. Grammar, conversation and exercises, with vocabulary for beginners. Cloth. 312 pages. $1.00.

Heath's German Dictionary. Retail price, $1.50.

Heath's Modern Language Series.

ELEMENTARY GERMAN TEXTS.

Grimm's Märchen and Schiller's Der Taucher (van der Smissen). With vocabulary. *Märchen* in Roman type. 65 cts.

Andersen's Märchen (Super). With vocabulary. 70 cts.

Andersen's Bilderbuch ohne Bilder (Bernhardt). Vocabulary. 30 cts.

Campe's Robinson der Jüngere (Ibershoff). Vocabulary. 40 cts.

Leander's Träumereien (van der Smissen). Vocabulary. 40 cts.

Volkmann's Kleine Geschichten (Bernhardt). Vocabulary. 30 cts.

Easy Selections for Sight Translation (Deering). 15 cts.

Storm's Geschichten aus der Tonne (Vogel). Vocabulary. 40 cts.

Storm's In St. Jürgen (Wright). Vocabulary. 30 cts.

Storm's Immensee (Bernhardt). Vocabulary. 30 cts.

Storm's Pole Poppenspäler (Bernhardt). Vocabulary. 40 cts.

Heyse's Niels mit der offenen Hand (Joynes). Vocab. and exercises. 30 cts.

Heyse's L'Arrabbiata (Bernhardt). With vocabulary. 25 cts.

Von Hillern's Höher als die Kirche (Clary). With vocabulary. 25 cts.

Hauff's Der Zwerg Nase. No notes. 15 cts.

Hauff's Das kalte Herz (van der Smissen). Vocab. Roman type. 40 cts.

Ali Baba and the Forty Thieves. No notes. 20 cts.

Schiller's Der Taucher (van der Smissen). Vocabulary. 12 cts.

Schiller's Der Neffe als Onkel (Beresford-Webb). Notes and vocab. 30 cts.

Goethe's Das Märchen (Eggert). Vocabulary. 30 cts.

Baumbach's Waldnovellen (Bernhardt). Six stories. Vocabulary. 35 cts.

Spyri's Rosenresli (Boll). Vocabulary. 25 cts.

Spyri's Moni der Geissbub. With vocabulary by H. A. Guerber. 25 cts.

Zschokke's Der zerbrochene Krug (Joynes). Vocab. and exercises. 25 cts.

Baumbach's Nicotiana (Bernhardt). Vocabulary. 30 cts.

Lohmeyer's Der Geissbub von Engelberg (Bernhardt). Vocab. 40 cts.

Elz's Er ist nicht eifersüchtig. With vocabulary by Prof. B.W. Wells. 25 cts.

Carmen Sylva's Aus meinem Königreich (Bernhardt). Vocabulary. 35 cts.

Gerstäcker's Germelshausen (Lewis). Notes and vocabulary. 25 cts.

Wichert's Als Verlobte empfehlen sich (Flom). Vocabulary. 25 cts.

Benedix's Nein (Spanhoofd). Vocabulary and exercises. 25 cts.

Benedix's Der Prozess (Wells). Vocabulary. 20 cts.

Zschokke's Das Wirtshaus zu Cransac (Joynes). Vocabulary and English Exercises. 30 cts.

Zschokke's Das Abenteuer der Neujahrsnacht (Handschin). Vocab. 35 cts.

Arnold's Fritz auf Ferien (Spanhoofd). Vocabulary. 25 cts.

Heyse's Das Mädchen von Treppi (Joynes). Vocab. and Exercises. 30 cts.

Stille Wasser (Bernhardt). Three tales. Vocabulary. 35 cts.

Heath's Modern Language Series.

INTERMEDIATE GERMAN TEXTS. (Partial List.)

Heath's Modern Language Series.

INTERMEDIATE GERMAN TEXTS. (Partial List.)

Schiller's Geschichte des dreissigjährigen Kriegs. Book III. With notes by Professor C. W. Prettyman, Dickinson College. 35 cts.

Schiller's Der Geisterseher. Part I. With notes and vocabulary by Professor Joynes, South Carolina College. 30 cts.

Selections for Sight Translation. Fifty fifteen-line extracts compiled by Mme. G. F. Mondan, High School, Bridgeport, Conn. 15 cts.

Selections for Advanced Sight Translation. Compiled by Rose Chamberlin, Bryn Mawr College. 15 cts.

Benedix's Die Hochzeitsreise. With notes and vocabulary by Natalie Schiefferdecker, of Abbott Academy. 25 cts.

Aus Herz und Welt. Two stories, with notes by Dr. Wm. Bernhardt. 25 cts.

Novelletten-Bibliothek. Vol. I. Six stories, selected and edited with notes by Dr. Wilhelm Bernhardt. 60 cts.

Novelletten-Bibliothek. Vol. II. Selected and edited as above. 60 cts.

Unter dem Christbaum. Five Christmas stories by Helene Stökl, with notes by Dr. Wilhelm Bernhardt. 60 cts.

Hoffmann's Historische Erzählungen. Four important periods of German history, with notes by Professor Beresford-Webb. 25 cts.

Wildenbruch's Das edle Blut. Edited with notes and vocabulary by Professor F. G. G. Schmidt, University of Oregon. 25 cts.

Wildenbruch's Der Letzte. With notes by Professor F. G. G. Schmidt of the University of Oregon. 25 cts.

Wildenbruch's Harold. With introduction and notes by Prof. Eggert. 35 cts.

Stifter's Das Haidedorf. A little prose idyl, with notes by Professor Heller of Washington University, St. Louis. 20 cts.

Chamisso's Peter Schlemihl. With notes by Professor Primer of the University of Texas. 25 cts.

Eichendorff's Aus dem Leben eines Taugenichts. With notes by Professor Osthaus of Indiana University. 35 cts.

Heine's Die Harzreise. With notes by Professor Van Daell of the Massachusetts Institute of Technology. 25 cts.

Jensen's Die braune Erica. With notes by Professor Joynes of South Carolina College. 25 cts.

Holberg's Niels Klim. Selections edited by E. H. Babbitt of Columbia College. 20 cts.

Lyrics and Ballads. Selected and edited with notes by Professor Hatfield, Northwestern University. 75 cts.

Meyer's Gustav Adolfs Page. With full notes by Professor Heller of Washington University. 25 cts.

Sudermann's Johannes. Introduction and notes by Prof. F. G. G. Schmidt of the University of Oregon. 35 cts.

Sudermann's Der Katzensteg. Abridged and edited by Prof. Wells. 40 cts.

Dahn's Sigwalt und Sigridh. With notes by Professor Schmidt, the University of Oregon. 25 cts.

Keller's Romeo und Julia auf dem Dorfe. With introduction and notes by Professor W. A. Adams of Dartmouth College. 30 cts.

Hauff's Lichtenstein. Abridged. With notes by Professor Vogel, Massachusetts Institute of Technology. 75 cts.

ZEBRA FINCHES
KW-055

Acknowledgments

A. A. Pare of Miami, Florida and Garrie Landry of Franklin, Louisiana helped me obtain some of the birds I needed. J. A. W. Prior of the Zebra Finch Society, London, England graciously permitted the Standards and Show Cage Specifications of the Society to be included in this book.

My wife Edith May patiently typed the manuscript and ferreted out a tremendous number of spelling errors; I hope she caught the worst of them.

Mervin F. Roberts
Old Lyme, Connecticut

Contents

Introduction, 8
Zebra Behavior, 20
Colors, 32
Life Cycle, 42
Nutrition, Water, and Bathing, 46
Housing, 64
Illness, 80

Photographers: *Michael Gilroy, Ray Hanson, Paul Kwast, Harry V. Lacey, Dan Martin, M.F. Roberts, W.A. Starika.* **Artists:** *R.A. Vowles, Heinzel.*

Front endpapers:*Zebra finches are hardy, active birds and many people enjoy breeding them.*

ZEBRA FINCHES

MERVIN F. ROBERTS

Through selective breeding and application of genetic principles, pied (left), fawn (below),white (facing page, middle bird), and many other color and pattern varieties have been developed—but they are all one-hundred percent zebra finch.

Zebras are relatively inexpensive to maintain.

People who have studied the pet industry will generally agree that, nine out of ten times, the initial purchase in a pet shop is an impulsive purchase of a living thing. Hardly anyone (at least in the U. S. A.) first buys a book to research the subject, then purchases the empty aquarium and finally gets the fish. Same goes for birds. You chose a zebra finch or two. Then you bought a cage or resolved to use that old canary cage sitting forgotten on a shelf for lo, these many years. Then you bought this book. Well, that's still all right. Even without the book, you made a wise decision when you chose zebra finches. They are hardy, inexpensive to maintain, long-lived, active and attractive. With your permission (and little else) they will breed even in a relatively small cage. They are quiet at night; they don't smell. They come in several color patterns, they get along well with each other and with many other cage birds also.

They are good for beginners but are nevertheless favorites of many advanced aviculturists. They tolerate wide fluctuations in temperature; if their bath water freezes, you have but to break the ice and they will be in and splashing. They thrive on inexpensive millet supplemented by items from your kitchen. You should have started with zebra finches long ago!

There is no need to describe here the feathering, colors and markings on zebra finches. The pictures and the Zebra Finch Society Standards do a better job, so let's just look at the branch of the tree of life where the little bird sits, because I believe this is a good way to begin a proper introduction.

Animalia—the animal kingdom, which includes all living things except plants and fungi.

Chordata—the phylum with dorsal nervous systems.

Vertebrata—the subphylum with bones or cartilage around these dorsally located nerves. Some older books call it a phylum.

Craniata—with a skull at one end of the vertebrae, an optional subphylum.

Aves—the class of birds, warm-blooded, feathered, egg-laying. There are 27 or 28 orders of birds and among them 9,000 or so species.

Passeriformes—the order of perching birds. There are 5,100 species, distributed among 74 families. Three toes point forward and one points to the rear. There are no webs on the feet. Young are blind and helpless when hatched.

Estrildidae—a family or a subfamily of weavers. Estrildid weavers include waxbills, grassfinches and mannikins. Here we find zebras, Java sparrows and mannikins. Some classifiers disagree and have placed zebras in another family.

Spermestidae—another suggested name for the family of grassfinches which includes

zebras and many other Australian finches.

Ploceidae—this family includes the "true" weavers, widowbirds and sparrows. Let us in this book assume that the zebra is either a Spermestidae or an Estrildid weaver rather than a

Adult zebra finches enjoy perching on twigs or dowels.

Side and front views of a gray male zebra (above). Back and front views of a fawn male (below). A yellow-billed fawn female (inset).

Two views of a gray female (above). A yellow-billed gray female (inset). Two views of a fawn female (below).

Introduction

Ploceid weaver. Eventually the problem will be resolved, but this is not the place.

Taeniopygia—one of the generic names currently used for the zebra finch. Note that this is one currently popular generic name, not necessarily the name for all time.

Taeni—means with a fillet or headband or ribbon and *pygia* means relative to the rump. I assume then that "ribbon rumped" refers to the narrow white rump stripe of the zebra finch. Most people would never notice it.

Guttata—the specific name. It means "with drop-like spots" and perhaps this was chosen to describe the white dots on the chestnut flanks of the male zebra finch or perhaps it refers to the white marks on tails of both sexes.

Castanotis—is another specific or subspecific name which refers to either the chestnut cheek or chestnut flank color of the male zebra finch. For a while some fanciers did call it the chestnut-eared finch, but that's past history.

Poephila—another of the generic names currently used for the zebra finch. *Poephila* means lover of grass.

Everyone knows what a zebra finch is, even if taxonomists disagree about the scientific name.

In the past 160 years this bird has had but two common English names, but let's see how the scientists have treated it.

There is some evidence that a zebra finch was exhibited in Paris in 1805, but it was not until 1817 that the record became unequivocal since it was then described scientifically and named by Viellot. Twenty years later that great explorer and naturalist, Gould, referred to it in his *Synopsis of Birds of Australia* and he called it *Amadina castanotis.* Later Gould renamed it *Taeniopygia castanotis.* Subsequently Gould was thought to be wrong and the little bird was renamed *Poephila guttata,* but this name, it turned out, was already assigned to another bird, however very closely related. So our Australian zebra finch was then relegated to subspecies rank as *Poephila guttata castanotis,* but many authors still call it *Taeniopygia guttata.* At least six names since 1837— that's not bad for a bird only four and a half inches long! So, then, in the literature you will find references to:

Fringilla guttata—Viellot 1817
Amadina castanotis—Gould (1837)
Taeniopygia guttata castanotis—Gould (after 1837)
Poephila guttata—Subsequent to Gould
Poephila guttata castanotis—Prior to Rutgers

Taeniopygia guttata—Rutgers 1964

Poephila castanotis—*Larousse Encyclopedia of Animal Life* (1967)

and all refer to the same bird, the zebra finch. Another common name adopted and later rejected by most fanciers is chestnut-eared finch. Call it a zebra and everyone will know

homogenous. There is just this one species inhabiting all Australia excepting only some coastal forest and marshy areas in the south, east and north. Several races within the species have been described by Mathews but these variations are not meaningful to birdkeepers.

One time-consuming

Here is a healthy young zebra finch. Note the full crop.

what you are talking about. Dr. Klaus Immelmann tells us that the Germans say *Zebrafink,* the French say *Diamant mandarin* and the Dutch call it *Zebravink.*

Zebra finches are found naturally wild over 90% of the subcontinent of Australia. This is a tremendous area for one species to range and still remain

diversion for writers of natural history is a study of the existing literature. Here we can find amusing and distressing contradictions deserving solution by Agatha Christie or Ellery Queen or Edgar Allan Poe. For example, Cyril Rogers in 1977 wrote a book entitled *Zebra Finches,* and in this otherwise excellent book there is a colored map showing the range of the zebra finch. Here we find the zebra on Tasmania, Sumba, Timor, and on the *coastal* parts of Australia excepting the south-

These zebra pairs (left and below) exhibit the basic gray, wild coloration, also called normal. The black-and-white barred tail is distinctive and adds a lot of sparkle to a cage or aviary since these birds are usually very active.

The zebra markings on the male's throat are evident here. However, the bill of the female is usually lighter than that of the male, particularly when she is mature.

central and west-central coasts. The center of the subcontinent is not inhabited by zebra finches, according to the map in Rogers' book. Of course, this map is absolutely wrong.

G. W. Iles wrote a book recently which is not dated. It is entitled *Breeding Australian Finches,* published by Isles d'Avon Ltd. In this book we find a map with shaded areas which show the same zebra finch inhabiting the same islands of Timor and Sumba as in Rogers', but not Tasmania (there are over 26,000 square miles in Tasmania). Furthermore, on his map of Australia, Iles correctly and accurately indicates that zebra finches inhabit the entire interior (approximately two million square miles) and most of the west coast, but he has no zebras on virtually all of the remaining *coastal* land that they occupy according to Cyril Rogers' map. Most interestingly, Iles' accurate map and Rogers' text are in very close agreement.

To the north of Australia and southwest of New Guinea lie the islands of the Lesser Sundas, Flores, Sumba and Timor and it was here that the aforementioned *Poephila guttata* (also sometimes called *Taeniopygia guttata guttata)* was found. This subspecies is not domesticated to the degree that the Australian zebra is, but it has been imported and exhibited

from time to time. These birds are larger than our caged zebras and the colors are darker. The bars on throat and breast are less pronounced. Some authorities designate it *Poephila guttata*, a wild subspecies of the native species of Australia, sometimes called *Taeniopygia guttata.* Obviously the nomenclature is wrong; both should be either in the genus *Poephila* or genus *Taeniopygia* and subspecific (trinomial) names should be assigned.

Taeniopygia will probably lose out to *Poephila* in this situation because *Poephila* seems to be the earlier designation. The word *Poephila* is reasonable for the zebra finch. Grass lover is really a good generic name for a little finch that builds grass nests and eats grass seeds.

WILD ZEBRAS

All of Australia (except some coastal and tropical forested areas) is home to the zebra, and this makes it as common a sight as the English (or house) sparrow is in the U.S.A. The wild Australian zebra finch looks much like our gray (or normal) domesticated zebra except that wild birds are said to have reddish eyes while the domesticated strain has brown eyes.

Dr. Klaus Immelmann suggests that the various

The claws on these birds are of normal length and do not have to be clipped.

populations of this vast continent are not differentiated into subspecies because the periodic droughts force the birds to move into new areas from time to time and this causes the various stocks to interbreed. He goes on to tell us that this most common bird adapts to a variety of wild habitats. Additionally, it does well near people. As a result colonies of birds build up near water tanks and cattle watering troughs. It is also found, he says, near houses, orchards, gardens, cultivated fields and pastures.

They need water for drinking and bathing, so the native bushmen regard them as a good sign of water nearby. Their food in the wild is reported to be half-ripe and ripe grass seed. Poa-grass is a favored food. Incidentally, Kentucky blue grass is also in this genus of Poa-grasses. Additionally, wild zebras eat insects. Flying termites and fly pupae are eaten avidly by wild Australian zebra finches.

The Australian government has banned the export of its finches, and perhaps all other birds as well, but this does not adversely affect the zebra finch hobby throughout the world since there is plenty of genetic material available in the birds held in captivity all over the rest of the world.

A gray penguin male (above). A fawn penguin male (below)—note how dilute the fawn color is in this specimen.

A gray penguin female (above). A fawn penguin female (below).

Zebra Behavior

Let's look at a large cage or aviary of zebras and make a list of the things that we should expect normal healthy zebras to do.

Action. They will be active most of the daytime. They will flitter and twitter and preen themselves and each other. Adults will feed the juveniles and juveniles will screech for food as though they were starving. There will be some quiet periods during the daylight hours. The birds will then perch singly or in small groups and snooze or just look around. These rest periods might last as long as a half-hour.

Bathing. Zebras will bathe daily or even twice daily. They will prefer to do this when the sun is bright, and after a moment of shaking off the loose water, they will dry and preen in direct sunlight.

Eating. Zebras will eat on and off all day. They will slack off about an hour before they go to roost for the night.

Roosting. They seem to crave a closed place to sleep at night. Pairs will often roost together in their nest with their eggs or fledglings or in a spare nest if the fledglings are so large as to use up all the room.

Noises. No one, however much he likes zebras, can call the birds melodious—they make a great volume and variety of noises that seem to mean something to each other. This goes on all during the daylight hours. There is variety to the sounds they make. Fledglings scream for food and adults chirp or squeak. No bird keeper would own a zebra finch simply to enjoy its song. Happy, healthy zebras are not silent.

The zebra finch, native to Australia, is capable of producing a variety of noises which often are quite loud.

Territories. They do stake out claims for territory in and around their nests but unless you crowd them, there is not any serious bullying around the feeder or the water.

Pair Bonds. They seem to form long-lasting or perhaps permanent pair bonds. If one of a pair dies, the other will re-mate, maybe not tomorrow, but soon.

Curiosity. Zebras are full of it. One would have to go to crows or hookbills (parrots and parrot-like birds) to find more inquisitive birds. If you put any device in a cage, they will be on it and, if possible, in it within minutes.

Reproduction. They are quite sexy. During their waking hours (unless they are resting, eating, bathing, feeding their young or preening) the chances are good that what they are doing somehow relates to reproduction. Nesting materials will be collected. Nest sites will be explored. Males will court their mates. Nests will be constructed. This is a big thing with healthy normal zebras— twelve months of the year.

Molting. There will be no dramatic molting of plumage among healthy normal zebra finches. They will look the same all year long. When they do molt it will be just a few feathers at a time and no bird will ever look especially patchy. Even the juvenile, as it matures, will develop adult coloration gradually.

A heavy molt is a sign that your birds are ill or that you have made a sudden (and ill-advised) environmental change. If this

Zebras are a good choice for the beginning breeder.

The color dilution that characterizes many zebra mutations appears in this cream male (above). A female zebra photographed in the wild (below).

A chestnut-flanked pair. Compare them with the cream male on the opposite page (top).

should happen, be sure that your birds are amply furnished with a wide variety of food supplements and that they are protected from drafts. Bear in mind that healthy zebras will thrive in unheated aviaries if they have warm draft-free roosts and plenty of proper food, including oily seeds. They can even survive some intermittent intense cold if not subjected to wetness or draft.

The birds in my aviary voluntarily and avidly go out of doors every day of the year—and this is in New England!

Sociability. Zebra finches get along well with other birds. They also get along well with people. A zebra will not likely become as intimate with you as a parrot but it certainly will get to recognize you, and perhaps even land on your finger or shoulder.

Another social aspect of the zebra finch fancy is that it brings people together. People will visit you to see your birds and you will visit them to see theirs. You will go to shows, join a club, subscribe to a magazine, write letters and easily become involved in a great hobby.

Hardiness. Zebras are tough. They will even thrive in an aviary where their drinking water is frozen every morning, so long as you provide them with a couple of chances to drink every day. They will live for years without disease. The only handling some may need is an occasional nail

clipping. In my experience, zebra finches are tougher than society finches or budgies or canaries.

THE PECKING ORDER

Chickens are famous for their henhouse and barnyard pecking orders, and psychologists have climbed the ladder of academic acclaim by writing papers about these pecking orders. It goes on everywhere, all the time.

When the pecking order syndrome is applied to zebra finches, you will discover that a single pair does well together. Three or four pairs stimulate each other to breed more frequently BUT with two pairs or an odd bird in a small group, you may experience trouble.

A simplistic explanation is that zebras cannot count too much over four or five. A cage or an aviary with a half dozen birds will not have a pecked or picked-on bird on the bottom of the ladder because no other bird remembers which is which.

I'm reminded of the dreaded piranha of the Amazon River which, when kept in an aquarium must be solitary since it will destroy or be destroyed. There was for many years a display tank in the Shedd Aquarium, Chicago with three or four dozen of these fish. Even though (now and then) one might get nipped, there was no widespread mayhem. If, however, the fish were separated into groups of

Zebra finches are active during most of the daytime but they do enjoy short rest periods. Sometimes they will perch singly; sometimes they will perch in small groups as pictured above.

perhaps three, the results would surely be fatally bloody.

So, keep a pair or keep a half-dozen or more birds, but avoid some number in between.

CROWDING

All of us know that many creatures are social. There are butterflies that migrate together and snakes that hibernate

A white zebra hen (above). One of these zebras has a ragged tail, and the other is squatting on its perch. Neither should be entered in a show.

This gray male zebra finch is almost perfect, but show standards may require that he be banded.

Caring for and watching your zebra finches will give you many hours of enjoyment.

Zebras are social creatures that enjoy togetherness.

together and whales that swim together and wolves that run in packs together, and bats that hang in their caves together. Zebra finches do it too, but this doesn't mean that you can pack them in a cage or an aviary as the Portuguese pack sardines. In other words, just because they get along well with each other they should not be thoughtlessly crowded.

For one thing, the risk of loss from communicable disease is ever present, and it increases as the population increases. Then too there is the matter of territories. Watch the few birds you have. Each will favor a particular perch, a special position in the bath, the same roosting place every night, a nest site. This is their life!

For a rule of thumb, give each caged bird one square foot of floor space. In an aviary, you might squeeze three birds into every two square feet, but that's the practical limit.

A white male (above). A fawn male (below).

A white female (above). A fawn female (below).

Colors

This yellow zebra is one of many mutations that can occur in the species.

This chapter is sticky because the names of the colors and patterns are not universally accepted, because new colors and patterns are being developed all the time, and because the genetic principles that apply are not necessarily fully known. The companion book to this one is entitled *Breeding Zebra Finches;* there the genetics are explained in some detail. For the final, authoritative word on colors, you should read the Zebra Finch

Society standards, which are the same for Britain and the United States. Afterwards, I'll review briefly the many and overlapping names of the established colors.

STANDARDS OF THE ZEBRA FINCH SOCIETY
(Reprinted with their kind permission)

SHOW STANDARDS
CONDITION to be essential. Birds should not receive any award unless in perfect show condition. (Missing, ragged or soiled feathers, and missing claws or toes constitute show faults).

TYPE. Bold throughout and of the "Cobby" type, giving the birds a look of substance; wings evenly carried to root of tail.

MARKINGS (COCKS). Chest bar distinct and clear cut, *not less* than 1/8 in. wide and of even width throughout. Side flankings should be prominent, extending from wing butts to end of rump and decorated with round, clearly defined white spots. Beak coral red with feet and legs deep pink. All markings where applicable to be clear and distinct. Hens as for cocks less cheek patches, chest bar and side flankings; beak a paler shade of red. Male markings on hens are definite show faults.

COLOUR STANDARDS

NORMAL COCK. Eyes dark. Beak red. Feet and legs red. Head and neck dark grey, wings grey. Breast bar jet black. Throat and upper breast zebra striped, grey with darker lines running from cheek to cheek continuing down to chest bar. Underparts white, may have some fawnish shading near vent and thighs. Cheek lobes dark orange. Tear markings black and distinct. Tail, black with white bars, side flankings reddish brown with clear white spots.

HEN. As for cock minus chest

Of all the domesticated birds, few are as attractive and diversified as the finch species.

barring, lobe and flank markings. Beak paler in colour. Tear markings black and distinct. A lighter shade of normal is recognised.

Show faults: Brown shading on wings and mantle.

WHITE, COCK AND HEN. Eyes dark. Beak red. Feed and legs pink. Pure white all over. Hens usually have beaks of a paler shade of red.

Show faults: Coloured spangles on mantle.

FAWN COCK. Eyes dark. Beak red. Feet and legs pink. Head, neck and wings deep even fawn. Breast bar dark. Throat and upper breast light fawn with zebra lines running from cheek to cheek continuing down to breast bar. Underparts white, may have some fawnish shading near vent and thighs, cheek lobes dark orange, tear markings same shade as breast bar. Tail dark barred with white. Side flankings reddish brown with even clear white spots.

HEN. As other hens but of the same shade of fawn as cocks.

Show faults: Variation in colour between cock and hen or pairs.

DOMINANT SILVER (DILUTE NORMAL) COCK. Eyes dark. Beak red. Feet and legs pink. There are various shades of dilute normals silvery grey being the ideal. Chest bars vary from sooty to pale grey, cheek lobes vary from pale orange to pale

cream, flanking from reddish to pinkish fawn with even clear white spots. Tear markings same shade as breast bar. The lighter the general colour the paler the chest, tail lobe and flankings. Tail dark with white bars.

HEN. As other hens but of the same shade to match the cocks.

Show faults: Variation in colour between cock and hen of pairs and variation in colour of individual birds. Fawn shadings. Indistinct markings on cocks.

DOMINANT CREAM (DILUTE FAWN) COCK. Eyes dark. Beak red. Feet and legs pink. Again all shades from deep cream to pale cream. Markings in cocks to be in general tone to match depth of diluteness. Tear markings same shade as breast bar. Tail deep cream with white bars.

HEN. As other hens but of the same shade to match the cocks.

Show faults: Variation in colour between cock and hen of pairs and variation in colour of individual birds. Fawn shadings. Indistinct markings on cocks.

PIED COCK AND HEN. Eyes dark. Beak red, feet and legs pink. Any other colours broken with white approximately 50% of each colour (white underparts not to be included in this 50%). Cock to retain cock markings in broken form on cheeks, flanks and chest. Tear markings distinct but can be broken.

Show faults: Loss of cock markings which should be shown

in broken form. Exhibition pairs
to be matched for Pied markings.
 CHESTNUT FLANKED WHITE
COCK. Eyes dark, beak red. Feet
and legs pink. Head, neck, back

Tree branches are good perches for
finches. The varying thickness enables
the bird to exercise its feet.

reddish brown with clear white
spots.
 HEN. As other hens to match
cocks. May have light head
markings. *Show faults:* Markings
too pale in the cock.
 PENGUIN (NORMAL) COCK.
Eyes dark. Beak red. Feet and
legs pink. Head, neck and wings
a light even silver grey, with

and wings as white as possible.
Underparts pure white. Breast
bar as near black as possible.
Tear markings same shade as
breast bar. Cheek lobes orange.
Tail white with bars. Colour to
match chest bar. Flank markings

flights, secondaries and coverts
edged with a paler shade of grey
giving a laced effect. (This lacing
does not show to full advantage
until the second full moult.)
Underparts from beak to vent
pure white without any trace of

barring. Cheek lobes pale orange to pale cream to match body colour of bird. Tail silvery grey barred with white. Side flankings reddish brown with clear white spots.

HEN. As other hens but with cheek lobes white. (There can be Penquin forms of the other colours.)

Show faults: Barring on chest.

RECESSIVE SILVER (DILUTE NORMAL) COCK. Eyes dark. Beak red. Feet and legs pink. Head, neck and mantle medium bluish grey, wings grey. Throat and upper breast zebra striped, bluish grey with darker lines running from cheek to cheek continuing down to chest bar. Chest bar dark grey. Tear marks distinct and to match colour of chest bar. Cheek lobes medium orange. Underparts white sometimes slightly shaded near thighs and vent. Flankings light reddish brown with clear white spots. Tail dark with white bars. Cock markings should be clear and distinct with only slight dilution.

HEN. As other hens but of the same shade to match the cocks.

Show faults: Variation in colour between cock and hen of pairs and variation in colour of individual birds. Fawn shadings. Indistinct markings on cock. Colour too dark or too light.

RECESSIVE CREAM (DILUTE FAWN) COCK. Eyes dark. Beak red. Feet and legs pink. Head,

neck and mantle medium cream, wings cream. Throat and upper breast zebra striped, cream with darker lines running from cheek to cheek continuing down to chest bar. Cheek lobes medium orange. Underparts white sometimes slightly shaded near thighs and vent. Flankings light reddish brown with clear white spots. Tail dark cream with white bars. Cock markings should be clear and distinct with only slight dilution.

HEN. As other hens but of the same shade to match the cocks.

Show faults: Variation in colour between cock and hen of pairs and variation in colour of individual birds. Fawn shadings. Indistinct markings on cocks. Colours too dark or too light.

YELLOW-BEAKED VARIETIES. General colouring as Normal Grey and all other mutations except the beak which should be shades of yellow with the cock birds showing the richest colour. There can be a Yellow-beaked form of all existing mutations and their composite forms. Yellow-beaks must be exhibited in true pairs of the same mutation.

Show faults: As with the normal red-beaked kinds.

A.O.C. In the interest of breeders and exhibitors no new colour will be recognised until thoroughly investigated by the Committee.

Panel Judges are reminded

A zebra hen's clutch may contain as many eggs as these.

that the *Show and Colour Standards must be observed.* Zebra Finches can only be shown in true pairs, i.e., a cock and a hen at Patronage Shows. A pair must always consist of two birds of the same mutation.

COLOR COMMENTS

Gray, normal wild. This color resembles the wild Australian zebra finch for all intents and purposes. Some see it as a bit brownish or a bit more or less ashy brown, but since Mathews described several races of wild birds, we will quickly get into some pretty involved circumlocution. Suffice it to say a gray must not have any irregular white feathers.

Gray is easy but few people can agree very long on the names of various other colors. Cyril H. Rogers, author of the *Encyclopedia of Cage and Aviary Birds,* an aviculturist for over forty years and 1978 President of the Zebra Finch Society (British) has this to say in the August 1978 Society Newsletter: "It is interesting to note that early Fawns were known as Cinnamons but the Dilute forms were always known as Creams. The name Fawn was apparently given to both Cinnamons when they were light and also to certain Silvers that showed a brownish shading above." Not only *interesting* but difficult, especially if all the books a

fancier owns were not written at the same time.

Incidentally, this bird which Cyril Rogers discusses is also sometimes called a fawn-brown or an Isabel. When you get to be an expert you too can coin a name or two. I advise you not to take these names too seriously as you get started in this hobby. The bird is so subtly variable in color it almost defies a simple description. Even the best color photos leave something to be desired.

One popular color pattern with several names is the absence of black. The male lacks any belly or breast markings. Call it a white throated or silverwing or penguin. The basic color will be diluted as well.

There are plenty of all-white zebra finches in pet shops and fanciers' cages, but at the time of this writing, none have pink eyes. Some have ruby red eyes and some have brownish red eyes or reddish brown eyes. Now the convention among students of genetics is to describe an albino as an individual which lacks all color pigment. The albino mouse is a good example. It has white hair and its eyes are not red; they are pink. Using the pink eye criterion, the 1980 white, red-eyed zebra finch is technically not an absolutely true albino. Dr. Matthew M. Vriends in his *Handbook of Zebra Finches*

This is one type of outdoor aviary for zebra finches. The sloped gutter (inset) is designed to channel rain water into a barrel, should the breeder wish to do so. The structure is set on concrete blocks, thus eliminating potential flooding problems and improving ventilation.

Colors

points this out and he chooses to call these birds pseudo-albino.

I look at nature in another way. I find few absolutes anywhere. Most living forms are literally and figuratively shades of gray. Therefore I call the red-eyed white an albino. I don't argue with Dr. Vriends; I simply see it differently and this is my book.

Some people have reported that there are blue zebra finches. Well, maybe. We already know that some (or perhaps all) black specimens are that way because of a dietary deficiency. Increase of vitamin D will result in lighter colors with their next set of feathers.

We also know that some bird exporters in the Orient have been coloring their birds with dyes, with sprays or baths for years. Canaries in Europe and the U.S.A. are sometimes fed on red foods so as to subsequently sprout reddish feathers.

Don't invest your life's savings in a breeding pair of purple zebra finches; they might just turn white or gray after their first molt.

Another group of color and pattern arrangements comes from hybrids. Since about two dozen related species have been hybridized with captive zebra finches, one can hardly imagine all the color and pattern combinations and permutations that are possible. Some are really beautiful. Most are sterile.

The gray wild natural zebra finch has surely produced color and feathering mutations in nature which made their bearers more conspicuous and vulnerable to attack by predators. These same mutations occur on a chance basis in the nests of cage birds as well, and here is where the bird keeper (with the help of Gregor Mendel and other geneticists) establishes new color varieties. The "feathering" I alluded to is a crest or crown or rosette of feathers on the top of the head. There are plenty of crested zebras in the hands of fanciers, but they don't stir up much excitement.

The progenitors of variously colored zebras may not have been perfectly pigmented but rather they were possibly light-colored birds and/or grays with but one or two light colored feathers. By thoughtful selective breeding, fanciers picked the birds which were mostly the desired color, and by inbreeding for this characteristic they finally achieved a pure (true breeding) strain. This is no "big deal." With most characteristics like this, it is just hard work for about fifty years. This is not long when we look at the time and effort that has gone into Jersey cattle, Percheron horses, Cocker Spaniels, Leghorn chickens, Siamese cats, Big Boy tomatoes or American Beauty roses.

Zebra varieties are not locked in, nor are they the sole property or privilege of any person or group of people. New colors or patterns crop up all over the birdkeeping world and you can, given the time and patience and a little understanding of genetic principles, "create" a distinctively different zebra finch. This is done in the same way that Henry Wallace "created" new varieties of corn or Paul Hahnel and Bill Sternke and Myron Gordon "created" new varieties of fish.

Actually man does not "create" these life forms. All he does is to use his God-given intelligence to sort out genetic material which mutated spontaneously or was latent for ages as a recessive trait and which simply required selective breeding to make it evident.

A holding cage housing a group of mixed finches.

Life Cycle

My companion book titled *Breeding Zebra Finches* covers this aspect in detail but here is a brief review. You may note that there are few things they always do and a few things they never do and many things they *may* do; their life style permits some rule-bending.

Zebras are social birds. They

After zebra finches reach maturity, it is easy to distinguish a male bird from a female bird.

This pair of lovely white zebras are the result of selective breeding.

travel in small flocks and nest near each other. The nest is frequently in a low shrub and it looks untidy outside. The twigs and coarse grass stems are woven somewhat but it is not neat outside as is a Baltimore Oriole's. Inside, it is lined with soft material; feathers, wool, vegetable down and soft grass are all commonly employed. The usual clutch consists of four

Life Cycle

white eggs. The eggs will hatch about two weeks after they were laid.

Both parents will spend the night in the nest. Zebras will sometimes build a nest to raise young and then build a second nest for roosting at night. They seem to prefer to roost in protected places.

The young will breed when they are hardly more than two months out of the nest. This is generally considered by aviculturists to be poor practice and so they separate the sexes to prevent the breeding of immature birds.

It would be very difficult for a person to estimate accurately the age of a zebra finch from the time it is six months old until it dies of old age, perhaps six or ten or even twelve years later.

SEX RECOGNITION
Female zebras probably identify males by how they behave since even all-white males seem to

have no trouble finding mates. All-white (self-whites), silvers and white pseudo-albino males have more red color in their bills than do the females—and that is the only difference apparent to people.

Juveniles, for the first 8 or 10 weeks after leaving the nest, look like females except that their bills are brown-black and gradually become coral or orange as they mature.

In the nest, juveniles are quite hairy or fuzzy and when the nest is lined with feathers (as is often the case), the newly hatched birds are frequently indistinguishable from their bedding.

Eggs of domestic birds are smooth, white and slightly chalky. They are slightly larger at one end, much in the manner of an ordinary hen's egg. No one has suggested a way to determine the sex of an unhatched chick. I'm not sure anyone cares.

Facing page: *Almost every color— and color combination—is represented in the feathering of various zebra finches.*

Nutrition, Water, and Bathing

Zebra finch diet is simple, but the basics must be available. No zebra can live on peanut butter and lettuce alone—however he may enjoy these things. The basic diet is the seed of a grass,

This is one of the newest zebra mutations: the Florida Fancy.

millet seed. Remember that one of the zebra's various generic names is *Poephila,* the lover of grass. There are several varieties, colors, and sizes of millet in the marketplace and you may find that the best source of

grain is your pet shop where you can obtain one-pound cartons of a "finch mixture." This consists of mostly millet with canary, rape, niger, oats and perhaps still other grains. If you have more than thirty birds, one-pound packages will not suffice; you should be getting your millet or finch mixture in bulk—perhaps 25 pounds or even 50 pounds at a time.

Which millet should you feed zebra finches? Try a few and settle for the one or two they favor. The nutrient values of all millets are about the same. The sizes and colors vary. Most of the color in millet is in the husk and your bird will remove the millet husk before he eats the grain anyway. Don't take millet color too seriously.

Buy clean grain—not damp, not water-stained, not moldy. It may have some webs in it, and if you watch patiently, you may see movement. Not quite as much as the movement of Mexican jumping beans, but movement nevertheless. The webs and the movement mean that there are little soft white or creamy colored grubs in your birdseed. These grubs are perhaps as large around as a pencil lead and they will grow to about five-eighths of an inch long. A grub of a web-moth has a cylindrical body with two rows of legs— much like a tiny inch-worm, except that they don't "inch," they simply creep about in the grain. Later, the grubs will pupate in cocoons and small moths will emerge to continue

their cycle of life. Your zebra finches may or may not eat the white web "worms" in the grain. Some aviculturists report that they do, and others report that they do not touch any insects. No harm in trying. If they do eat the web "worms", then offer them mealworms too.

You should test your grain to assure that it is alive. The

By looking at the throat markings on this bird, you can see where the zebra finch gets its name

viability of millet is much more important to your birds than is its color. Plant some as you would grass seed or put some on a wet towel for a few days to be sure that at least 75% of it germinates, that is, sprouts. Incidentally, your birds will enjoy eating sprouted grain as a diet supplement.

Although millet is the basic diet ingredient for seed-eating finches, its protein content is lower than what breeding and baby finches ideally should have. One problem is that millet lacks certain amino acids. This is why experienced bird keepers will offer a variety of oily seeds including rape, niger, poppy and sesame to supplement the basic millet diet. In case you wondered why oily seeds are recommended to increase protein in the diet, it is a fact that most high-fat seeds are also high in protein. Canary seed, a notable exception, is a good protein source even though it is not relatively high in oil.

Interestingly, canary seed, *Phalaris canariensis,* happens to be high in those amino acids which are correspondingly low in millet, *Panicum miliaceum.* It should also be mentioned here that spray millet is in fact not a *Panicum* but is classified in another genus of plants and is scientifically called *Setaria italica.*

One pitfall experienced by many beginning finch keepers is that of husks versus seeds. These birds don't carry whole seeds in their bills and they don't swallow them either. When a zebra finch picks up a grain of canary seed or a grain of millet, it positions and holds the grain between the upper and lower bill using its tongue to manipulate it. A squeeze or two pops the husk off in one or two parts and then the husked seed is swallowed. The husk then falls aside within an inch of the place it was picked up. Soon the seed dispenser or dish is full of inedible chaff and the birds could be starving. If your eyes are not sharp enough to discriminate between whole grain and husks, you might try blowing at the food dish—the chaff will be much lighter and since it is cup-shaped, it will tend to be caught in the airstream and carried off. If you keep several hundred birds you should buy a winnower; it will pay for itself in saved grain and you can give up the blowing.

An alternative to winnowing is simply to dump the chaff-laden grain into a tray of moistened earth where the chaff will become mulch and much of the remaining grain will sprout. Your birds will then consume in sprouted form what would otherwise be lost.

SPRAY MILLET
There is no shortage of bird

fanciers who are willing to buy spray millet for their birds at more than two dollars per pound, and in small quantities they will pay as much as three dollars a pound! They know that their birds love it.

Release your birds in a large sunny aviary and let them settle

if there are several species present. Then put a few stalks of spray millet in a weighted vase or hang a bundle from a wire and within minutes *all* the birds of *all* the species will be picking over that millet.

If you have trouble with that over-two-dollars-per-pound price

This eight-day-old baby is eagerly awaiting a meal.

down. Some will bathe, others roost, still others will pick at grit, preen, build nests or simply fly back and forth. There will be little or no uniform activity, especially

tag, you might try a late summer walk through a field. With a shopping bag and a pair of snippers you can gather all sorts of weeds that are going to seed. If you want to be scientific about it you should read two paperback Dover reprints:

Martin, Zim and Nelson, *American Wildlife and Plants,* New York, 1961.

These zebra finches are nibbling at a piece of grass sod. By doing so, they are picking up not only grits, but trace elements of minerals.

Knobel, Edward, *Field Guide to the Grasses, Sedges and Rushes of the U.S.,* New York, 1977.

Both of these books point out that spray millet or foxtail millet or bristlegrass or *Setaria italica* is the same species whether domesticated or wild. If you purchase a domestic farm grown product, you have the right to assume that it was not treated with any dangerous insecticide and of course if you harvest it from a field, you should know whether that field had been sprayed. Not likely, since no one wastes expensive sprays on weed fields. More importantly, cultivated millet tends to have larger seeds. The choice is up to you; regardless, the response from the birds will justify your expense or your effort.

FOOD SUPPLEMENTS

Among the supplements which your zebras may enjoy are honey and oranges. You might offer a slice of bread or toast moistened with a mixture of honey and orange juice or perhaps just one or the other.

Powdered yeast will stick to grain which was moistened with cod liver oil and this is a high fat, high protein, high vitamin D supplement which your birds could well be given occasionally.

Although, and this bears repeating, zebra finches can live out normal lives with minerals, grit, water and millet, this is much like a jailbird limited to bread and water. He will survive. Period.

So, sweeten the pot with green foods such as lettuce, spinach and celery tops, the supplements already mentioned, thirty minute hard-boiled eggs whole (with shells removed) or diced up with a fork or pushed through a strainer. Also offer foods derived from insects. Termites and silkworm pupae are nutritionally excellent but a bother to prepare. You can buy them from your pet dealer or through advertisements in the bird magazines. Don't stock a big inventory of insectile food until

you test a little of it. Your zebras may refuse to touch it, but if insect-eating birds are with the zebras in the same cage or aviary, your birds may learn to eat this high protein food as a supplement after watching the others do it.

Still another food supplement from which your zebras might benefit is dried seaweed. This is high in minerals and they may have a craving for it if a trace element is otherwise lacking in their diet.

As you read this book you may feel "snowed" by all the remarks about what zebra finches will eat. Really it isn't mandatory that you feed each item every day. The supplements are mostly optional. Your birds will survive and thrive and even breed on a diet of water, millet, grit, minerals and a little green food from time to time. As I mentioned previously, treats such as French toast and milk sop are like the frosting on the cake. One can manage without them but life is better when they are included.

Other more delicate cage bird species might not even survive without some supplements to the basic grain diet—for them these foods are not supplements; they are an integral part of the regular diet. On the other hand, the hardy zebra likes the supplements, does better for them, but does not require them for survival.

Nutrition, Water, and Bathing

During the course of writing and illustrating this book, an eight by twelve foot inside aviary with a connected three foot by six foot outside flight cage was home to about thirty zebra finches. They multiplied to the point where some were removed to avoid crowding. These birds were fed just once every 24 hours. The one dish for bath and drinking water was changed daily and about a cup of mixed canary seed and millet replaced the husks left from the previous day. About ¼ cup of soaked grain (canary and millet) "started" the previous morning was also offered sometimes. Additionally, one quarter to one-half a hard boiled chicken egg (sometimes broken up with a fork) *and* its crushed shell went into the aviary along with a leaf or two of green lettuce.

You might have noticed that I hedged a bit when I got to the fixing of the hard boiled egg. As a matter of fact, a whole (but shelled) hard boiled hen's egg will be eaten by zebra finches regardless of whether you chop it, dice it, sieve it or simply take off the shell and serve it whole. And when you serve it "whole" you may discover as I did that your finches prefer the white over the yolk.

The total time required to accomplish this feeding including washing of utensils was about ten minutes. If the same number of birds were caged as pairs, the time required would be more like the better part of an hour, daily.

GRAIN AND WATER STORAGE
If you store more than a pound of grain and if mice, web-worms, mealworms or other vermin are a nuisance, consider the plastic gallon milk container. It is free, easy to clean, easy to fill by the use of a funnel, and easy to seal. With it, moisture content and loss to insects will be under your control. A label with the description and source of the seed is easy to affix; additionally, you can quickly judge how much you have on hand. Don't store grain in bright sunlight; the ultra-violet rays will degrade the nutrient values.

These narrow-necked bottles are also handy for water if you have no plumbing in your aviary or bird room. An open bucket is an invitation to disaster by drowning. Just rinse the bottles thoroughly and don't neglect to wash and screw down the caps.

MINERALS
One problem for beginning bird keepers is that they neglect the few mandatory and vital things because it **all** looks so simple. A good example of this oversight is neglect of your birds' mineral requirements. No zebra can survive for long without minerals, but some individuals are able to

go for long periods without *ingesting* any. If the missing substance is critical, the existing supply stored in bones or blood or certain organs will be gradually depleted and the loss to the bird will take place so insidiously that you may never realize that sterility or poor plumage or death is imminent. The classic example of this is with the horse which was gradually trained to eat 100% pure sawdust. The trouble was that he dropped dead just when it looked like the experiment was a success. Your birds should have a mineral block or mineral grit mixture before them at all times. It should be situated so that it is accessible but so that it will not be covered with droppings. There is no need for you to make up this mineral mixture—there are plenty of good ones available from pet shops and cage bird supply houses. The major ingredients are sodium chloride (common salt—NaCl) and calcium carbonate (limestone—$CaCO_3$). The other ingredients are present as traces and include iron, copper, potassium, phosphorus, sulphur, iodine, and even that notorious poison, arsenic. All animal life, man included, requires virtually all the chemically reactive elements in carefully proportioned traces. Some will come from the grain and some be found in water,

Remember that fresh drinking water must be provided daily for your pet. A water font such as this one works well and is designed to prevent birds from soiling their drinking water.

vegetables, eggs or bread or other food supplements you provide, and some may not be there. The mineral block or grit is your insurance policy. Don't neglect it. Cuttlebone is both a beak sharpener and a source of calcium plus other important trace elements but cuttlebone is not a substitute for good mineral block or grit, properly proportioned to supply all the minerals and trace elements your bird needs.

Lime can come from whole or crushed cuttlebone, crushed oyster shells, crushed lime plaster out of a very *old* house, or crushed boiled or baked chicken egg shells. Most newer homes are plastered or wallboarded with gypsum plaster or gypsum wallboard (calcium sulphate), but one hundred years ago, hydrated lime was used for plastering. Hydrated lime became lime carbonate over the course of time and this mineral carbonate is what you should provide to your birds. Mineral grit put up especially for cage birds surely contains this chemical compound as well as traces of everything else that birds are known to require.

One reason cuttlefish bone is so highly regarded by experienced birdkeepers is to be seen in the following figures:

Eggshell of domestic chicken—85% calcium carbonate—1.4% magnesium carbonate

Cuttlefish bone—85% calcium carbonate—.5% magnesium carbonate

The reason for the word "crushed" in the previous paragraph is that some fanciers believe that a finch cannot satisfy its need for calcium by picking at large pieces of hard material. This is, of course, true if you offer a large block of

marble statuary or limestone building block, or even the shell of a cherrystone clam. Cuttlebone by contrast is so soft you can cut it with your fingernail; your zebras will have no trouble picking particles from the edges or soft side. Notice that every piece of cuttlebone does have a hard side and a soft side; if you hang it against a wall, expose the soft side. So, crush the stone and do whatever you think is right with the cuttlebone.

You may discover that the broken shells of those hard-boiled eggs you feed to your birds are favored over cuttlebone. This is great, so long as the shells were boiled for at least 1/2 hour—or baked over low heat in the oven. The reason is that some avian diseases are transmitted by way of raw eggs. A second reason is that it is not a good idea to suggest to a bird that raw birds' eggs are good bird food.

So, if you find that your birds crave even more shell than they get with their ration of hard-boiled eggs, save the shells from home cooking, but remember to boil or bake them for a half-hour before feeding.

One aspect of nutrition, well known, but frequently overlooked by beginners in aviculture is that calcium in bones and egg shells requires vitamin D in order to be properly utilized. That is why milk, a high calcium food, is

Many feathers are still in the sheaths of these zebra finch nestlings.

often "fortified" with vitamin D. This vitamin D then with calcium is the anti-rachitic or preventive for rickets, the disease of soft bones.

The natural chemical substance vitamin D is often called the "sunlight vitamin" because it is so closely tied in with solar rays. In fact, the process for making the vitamin D in milk hinges on irradiation (exposure) by certain wave lengths of ultra-violet light naturally emitted by the sun or artificially created by special electrical discharge lamps. The point is simply that direct unfiltered sunlight seems to help birds produce their own vitamin D. So, you should, if possible, give your birds the advantage of a screened aviary, part of which is exposed to direct sunlight a few hours daily. A more sophisticated technique would be to provide ultra-violet light from a lamp. This is difficult, expensive and could be dangerous if overdone. The third method is to provide foods and food supplements which are known to be rich in the various complex fractions of this important substance. You may, if you wish, supplement their diet by adding irradiated cod liver oil to some of the grain you feed, or you might use a vitamin D concentrate available from your pet dealer or pharmacist. As you can see, there are several routes to follow; choose the one that best suits your birds, and don't neglect it.

As an aside of considerable interest to people who avoid eating foods containing cholesterol, it should be pointed out that as long ago as 1924 studies of cholesterol and vitamin D showed that ". . .cholesterol, which accompanies most animal fats, and the analogous constituents of vegetable oils, became active antirachitically when they were exposed to ultra-violet radiation." All of this foregoing quotation is from the fourteenth edition of the *Encyclopaedia Britannica.* Actually it is not the cholesterol itself that is activated but a minor component associated with it and known as ergosterol.

Don't worry about cholesterol in your birds' diet causing heart disease. It is very likely that by the time you read this book there will be ample evidence to prove that the quantity of cholesterol that plugs your circulatory system or that of your pet bird has little or nothing to do with the quantity of cholesterol in the diet. Certain animals and people can and do manufacture cholesterol regardless of what they eat.

The other vitamins necessary for the health and fertility of your birds (A, B, C and E) will come naturally if you show intelligent

These are the eggs of a Lady Gouldian finch. Compare them with the zebra finch eggs below.

gizzard. Here, the seeds and an assortment of grains of sand are squeezed and churned and ground until the seeds break up into a mass of damp flour.

The bird chooses what it needs. You need only provide the grit. Your pet shop, bird store or nearby beach will furnish a supply. Keep it before the birds at all times.

You may also discover that zebras eat charcoal. Good! But the one is no substitute for the other.

VITAMINS

Let's go down the list of vitamins and related substances but don't

care in providing fresh raw green vegetables, a variety of living seeds (test them occasionally to be sure they sprout) and diet supplements such as fruit, hard boiled or scrambled eggs, and wheat germ.

GRIT

Zebra finches, and in fact all seed eaters, swallow whole grains. Small birds husk the seeds but larger species like pigeons, poultry and waterfowl swallow it whole. There is no chewing in the mouth; this is accomplished later in a powerfully muscular organ, the

This is the clutch of a zebra finch. Some breeders have found that a small clutch may hatch more quickly than a large one.

57

let it frighten you. A balanced and diversified diet will probably provide all the vitamins your birds will ever need and a vitamin supplement from your pet dealer will guarantee to provide these substances. Here then, for the record are their names, natural sources and the diseases of birds which develop when these vitamins are absent.

A—Found in eggs and green vegetables, it improves night vision and resistance to infection, especially of skin. It is possible that excessive dosing of vitamin A causes French molt in budgies.

B—This is the famous anti-Beri-Beri vitamin. Actually it is a "complex" of a dozen or so vitamins. Niacin, for example, is vital for growth and good plumage. Biotin improves egg hatchability.

C—This is the scurvy-preventive citrus fruit vitamin. Also called ascorbic acid. Seed-eating birds seem to manufacture it and so do not require any in their diet.

D—Calcium metabolism depends on vitamin D and the source of it is ultra-violet radiation on some oils and fats. Birds in direct sunlight make their own vitamin D.

E—Found in seed germs, it is destroyed through oxidation by excessive dosage of cod liver oil.

K—Required for coagulation of blood. Produced in the intestines by bacteria and so not required in the diet. Vitamin K is especially vulnerable to antibiotics.

Vitamins A, D, E and K are fat soluble and are often associated with edible oils or fats. Vitamins B and C are water soluble. It is entirely possible that indiscriminate dosing of cagebirds with antibiotics can actually destroy vitamins or at least reduce the ability of the bird to assimilate those vitamins it does ingest.

Water and Bathing

Zebra finches are not web-footed but they certainly love to have bathing water close by at all times. A tray or glass dish one inch deep and as large as possible is what they crave. The water depth should be about one-half inch. If the sides of the tray are but one-half inch deep, the loss due to splashing will make a mess. If the tray is much deeper than one inch, the birds will be inhibited, probably because the bath tub will seem too much like a trap. The birds want to jump in and then fly out easily.

Don't get the idea that because you furnish a drinking water dish and a bath water dish that they will use these facilities as you have planned. There will always be a bath water drinker and a drinking water bather. Don't fight it. Just try to keep all the water in the cage or aviary

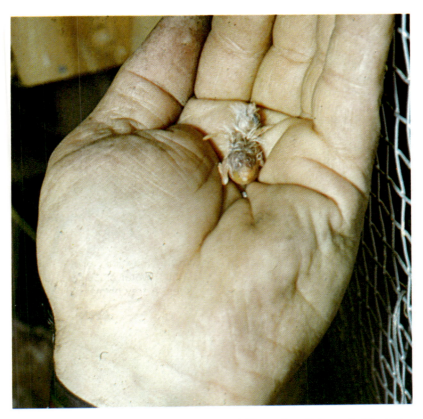

This zebra finch chick is about three days old.

clean and fresh.

That dish of bath water will teach you a lot about your birds. Watch it. Remember that they are inveterate bathers. If each adult zebra finch does not take a dip or two every day, look closely at the water. It is probably not clean enough for *you* to want to drink it. Rinse the dish and fill it with fresh, clean, cool water and most likely all those birds will be in it up to their rumps within minutes. This business of frequent bathing is true for society finches as well, but somewhat less so for many other cagebirds.

If your birds are provided with a bath and the water is fresh and clean and still they don't use it, look to its depth. These little fellows are pretty fussy about how far they wade in before the splashing. The simplest procedure is for you to provide a long bathtub and raise one end an inch and fill the tub until the

Try it, they'll like it.

Chlorine is frequently added to municipal water supplies to reduce odors and also to reduce the possibility of transmission of diseases. Some birds tolerate small amounts and others seem to resent it. Fortunately chlorine

These young birds are normal and healthy.

high end is barely wet. Then, somewhere over that sloped bottom, the water depth will be precisely what the birds prefer.

escapes into the air if water is left standing with a large surface exposed. Agitation helps. Boiling helps but is really unnecessary. If your tap water is heavily chlorinated, simply draw off what you need into a gallon plastic milk bottle—fill only up to the level where the bottle begins to neck down—say three quarts, and let it stand, uncorked for a day or two. Hot tap water will give up chlorine even faster. Let it stand until it cools, then use it.

Water temperature is not an issue with zebra finches. Serve it at room temperature or if cooler, it will soon reach room temperature. Same goes for bath water. Some zebras will bathe and splash twice daily if you leave water out for them. This is where anodized aluminum rustproof cages and trays earn their keep. Generally, the tray or the bottom of the cage gets most of the punishment from grits, bird droppings and water.

As mentioned elsewhere, but for added emphasis it is worth repeating here, your zebra finches will drink frequently and bathe frequently. They will bathe in their drinking water and drink from their bathing dishes. You may try to force them to do it your way. You probably will not succeed. Why bother? The water should be fresh and clean at all times.

Zebra finches can tolerate intermittent freezing temperatures, but water and some water containers cannot. Your birds will not freeze, but if there is nothing but ice available, they may die of thirst.

It is worth repeating that zebras crave a bath now and then. How frequently? Twice daily if the ice is thin enough to break through. To watch them rattle their wings and tails in a shallow dish of water is to watch birds in bliss. It is obvious to anyone who witnesses these ablutions that these birds are not acting out of duty or boredom or instinct but because they seem to take pleasure in splashing. When one jumps in, the others will follow and for about five minutes pandemonium prevails.

The birds will wet themselves to a point just short of where flying becomes difficult, and then they will flit off to a perch, preferably in bright sunlight for drying, fluffing and preening. The bathing accomplishes several things. It probably helps control lice. It carries off dirt and dead particles of skin and feathers. It moistens the feathers of birds which are incubating eggs and this moisture aids in the hatching process. When eggs with live embryos don't hatch, the fault is frequently with the moisture. Bear in mind that nests in cages don't get the benefit of rain or even the morning dew.

You may substitute a spray in a planted aviary or an outside flight for the bath dish or better still, offer both. For a species without webbed feet, it is really surprising how much zebras demonstrate their enjoyment of the bath.

If you house your birds in an outdoor aviary, you may discover that they capture ants and rub themselves with them, or that they stand over an anthill and permit the ants to crawl over themselves. The ants are of the non-stinging varieties and the birds known to do this include 200 species in 30 of the 56 passerine families. Whether zebras also indulge is for you to find out. At this moment, positive evidence is lacking.

If your birds do it, at least we think we know *why.* It seems that formic acid and other similar chemicals generated by many species of ants will keep lice away. Other liquids produced by ants may aid in feather maintenance. Among the Estrildidae, waxbills are known to "ant" and we know that some waxbills have hybridized with zebra finches, so you can go on from there.

Dust bathing is another activity your birds may indulge in if you provide the ingredients. Bone dry fine sand or earth is worked into the plumage and then it is shaken out, perhaps for feather maintenance or perhaps for louse control. Some species bathe first in dust and then in water when the situation permits. The common house sparrow, *Passer domesticus domesticus,* is a good example.

Sunbathing is another form of bathing zebra finches will indulge in whenever the opportunity affords. Really, they are very busy "doing things" all the daylight hours, but they are opportunists and when the sun shines, they will spread their feathers and soak in some sun rays. If the sunlight gets to your birds through a glass window it will have lost that vitally important ingredient, ultra violet, which is the form of radiant energy that triggers the creation of vitamin D. Every bird needs vitamin D for the assimilation of calcium and it may be derived from either direct exposure to sunlight (thus the bird manufactures the vitamin) or by supplements to the food. Your caging arrangements will determine which route to take. Or, take both.

Oiling is still another form of bathing for feather maintenance. Every finch has an oil gland at the base of its tail which it can reach with its bill. The gland is stimulated by rubbing to secrete oil and with its bill, the bird distributes the oil over its feathers. This tends to waterproof them, but the *exact* reason why they do it is not positively known. Some families of birds don't have oil glands, but somehow they do very nicely, even when it rains. There is also reason to believe that oiling has an insulating effect.

There are more color varieties of zebra finches available than any other finch.

Birds tend to fly horizontally; that is, they travel more horizontal distance than vertical distance in the course of a lifetime. So, you should provide a cage where the greatest distance is horizontal. If you have space and money for three cubic feet of cage, it would be better three feet long by a foot high and a foot wide than three feet high and a foot square on the base. This cage would be

One sign of good health in a bird is clean, clear eyes.

large enough for one pair to breed or for four birds to live together wholesomely. If you can provide a larger home for your pets, so much the better. Flying is good for them and maintenance is easier in larger quarters.

If you have direct sunlight available, this is great. Just remember not to let the sun cook your pets. They should always have some place in the cage or aviary where they can roost in the shade and they should also have cool, fresh bath water before them all the time or at least whenever they are exposed to the sun.

Buy a cage which is made of anodized aluminum or stainless steel, or chromium plated if you can afford it. In the long run these cages, available in most pet shops, will be the least expensive. Galvanized steel mesh is also durable but not as attractive in the home. A canary cage or a parakeet cage will house a zebra finch as well, but if you have a choice, choose the cage designed for this bird— eventually you may wish to breed zebras and then a large long cage will make a fine breeding establishment.

If you plan on an outdoor ground-level aviary, wonderful! Finches do well in them, especially if they are planted with tough plants. A tender leaf will end up on the floor. Try fruit trees, forsythia and privets. Be sure you have buried galvanized wire mesh deeply (at least a foot) so as to keep out rats, weasels, cats, vermin and other predators.

The ideal screening is three-eighths-inch square mesh (or three eighths by one inch). Most adult zebras will not get through one-half by one-inch mesh (or one-half by one-half). Three-eighths square seems to keep all birds in and all mammals out.

Incidentally, mice are not predators. They don't bite the birds, but nevertheless they can cause the birds to die. Mice are nocturnal and zebras are diurnal, so the zebras (which are caged and unable to get away) will be kept awake until they waste away from lack of sleep. Mice also foul the grain. Call them vermin.

The cage or aviary should have provisions for food, drinking water, bathing water, grit, perching, nesting (if this is what you have in mind) and a place to hang a cuttlebone. Not too difficult or costly when you consider the pleasure these birds will provide.

At night your birds will enjoy roosting in a nest box even if they are not breeding. If you have room in their cage, give them a coconut or a coffee can or a wicker basket. During the day, they will perch on twigs or dowels but you should not force them to use perches with

Regular nest inspections are important.

sandpaper. Keep it as natural as you can.

If you place potted plants in your large cage or aviary, the birds certainly will spend a lot of time perching, picking, and climbing. You should aim at something tough and not poisonous. A fruit tree or a privet or a forsythia or a honeysuckle bush might be good to try. If there is not room for a tree,

Facing page, above: *A zebra hen broods her newly hatched chicks.* **Facing page, below:** *This is what happens if you don't provide plenty of extra nests. This basket is overloaded with grass and the eggs of several hens.* **Above:** *Here a pair of penguin breeders sit atop their overstuffed nest box. Zebras are great for overstuffing their nests.*

Housing

settle for a twig. Red and white cedars are evergreen but a bit coarse. One four-foot cedar tree in the author's aviary boasted never fewer than two well built and productive nests. Don't spend a lot of money on the tree and don't waste your effort on something which is in flower—you may discover that your zebras prefer to have the petals and leaves on the floor, and they will surely accomplish their version of interior decoration in spite of your best laid plans.

By comparison with society finches, you may find that your zebras are somewhat better off in aviaries whereas societies do better in 30 or 36 inch cages—with respect to production.

Cages can be designed for economy of cleaning and feeding effort or for economy of construction or for economy of space. Obviously if you slice the pie thinly enough you would do better with a stuffed bird or a carving or a really good photograph.

On the other hand, caging can become an architectural or decorative part of your home. A large cage can be created to serve as a room divider. Remember, as you plan such a project that you will need to remove birds, feed and water them, furnish bath facilities, and perching accommodations. You might opt for potted plants as perches and again you should

make the doors large enough to get those plants in and out.

Partitions or restraints for the birds are traditionally made of wire mesh or rods but raffia also provides security and in certain decorative schemes it should prove especially attractive. Glass is easy to look through but of course it doesn't permit circulation of air and it also mutes any sounds. If either or both of the walls which are close together—say, no more than eighteen inches apart—the risk of injury to a bird by flying into a transparent window is not great. For one thing, your birds will quickly learn to do most of their flying the "long" way and also it would be hard even for a finch to pick up much speed in those narrow confines. Fortunately too zebra finches are not high-strung.

Pests and Enemies

Pests include wild birds, mice, rats, cats, and small boys. A young mouse, for instance, can sometimes squeeze through half-inch square screening and by scurrying around at night, rob your birds of sleep and even cause them to hurt themselves as they fly blindly into objects at night. Your birds will not successfully produce clutches of maximum numbers if they are

The normal zebra is distinguished by the bold black-and-white markings on its tail.

harassed at night by mice or other creatures. You must assure them of a quiet night, every night.

Make up your mind before you invest too much cash or time—do you want to maintain a collection of healthy birds or do you wish to show them off to all comers—smokers, coughers, sneezers, cage rattlers, shouters, and arm wavers included?

Escapes are easy for all finches, especially zebras. They are inquiring, probing, searching, all day long. If an opening one inch in diameter exists anywhere, they will find it and be out even if they don't really want to go anywhere in particular. If you build an aviary, make the doors as low as you can conveniently bend under. Many escapes take place over your head when a high door is opened. Corridors and arrangements of double doors are ideal for prevention of escapes. The trouble is that you have to open and close twice as many doors in order to make a visit.

When frightened, your aviary birds will fly toward the light, and if the light happens to be coming through a glass window, broken necks and fractured skulls could result. Usually prevention is easy to accomplish. Stretch a cheese-cloth-like fabric over the inside of the window and fasten it to the

Facing page, top and bottom: *Zebras seem to like to do things such as feeding together, whether it's a leaf of romain lettuce or their seed mix.* **Above:** *The quality of this zebra's diet shows in his perfect condition.*

frame with thumbtacks or
staples. Most of the light will still
get in but collisions will be
cushioned.

Another alternative is to
"paint" the window glass inside
with a powder type cleanser
such as "Bon Ami" or calcimine
whitewash. These materials
even if applied thinly will suffice
to warn the birds. Of course, the
cheese-cloth offers real
protection; the painting is merely
a warning.

VISITORS

You should be seen by your
zebras. Visit them daily—during
the light hours. If you breed a
few, handle the babies once their
eyes are open, if only to get
bands on them. These birds have
been with humans for a long
time and they seem, instinctively,
to get along well with us. They
will not become as intimate with
you as a budgie or a parrot, but
as you care for your birds, you
will notice that you are trusted.
We all know (and birds know
instinctively) that they are
vulnerable when they bathe. It is
not easy to take off from a
muddy wet surface and it is not
possible to fly at top speed with
wet feathers. Nevertheless, your
birds will bathe while you watch
them. Under similar
circumstances a cordon bleu or
an orange-cheeked waxbill would
be less likely to bathe with

someone hovering nearby.

Cagebirds do well with routine.
So, create a routine and then try
to live with it. Cage cleaning,
feeding, nest inspection and
casual visits should all be during
the bright light hours, regardless
of whether the light is daylight or
artificial. Don't let daylight dim
and then suddenly turn on
brilliant electric lights and expect
your birds to appreciate your
company. Most zebras will
probably tolerate the shock, but
rare or delicate species could
easily keel over after a few such
experiences.

Noise is also a problem you
will have to cope with. Again,
your birds will adjust to
conditions which build up
gradually and then repeat
themselves at predictable
intervals. Look at birds and bats
in a belfry. Every hour on the
hour a two-ton bronze bell is
struck by a hundred pound cast
iron hammer and all day long the
bats sleep through it and all
night long the birds sleep
through it. And on Sunday
morning at ten or eleven o'clock
the call to worship is deafening;
yet these animals come back day
after day, for generations.
Routine disturbances are really
not disturbances.

If you breed your birds (and
this is not especially difficult)
decide early on that you will look
in the nest once daily, or that you
will stay strictly away for the

Their parents will give these babies all the care they need.

entire six weeks from first egg to flying fledgling. These precautionary notes will be no great imposition on you—but if you are aiming to take that step from owning a cage of birds to becoming a bird keeper, this is how to begin. Here is where we separate the men from the boys, the sheep from the goats, the bird owners from the bird keepers.

CAPTURES

First, to avoid any possible misunderstanding, do not trap or even possess any wild trapped native finches in the U.S.A. It is against federal law to own or traffic in native wild birds. A Philadelphia lawyer might find a few loopholes, but a Philadelphia judge might find the lawyer was wrong. So, to keep out of jail, just don't catch or possess native birds. On the statute

Facing page, top and bottom: *A pair of silvers.*
Fawn male (upper bird) and silver female. **Above:**
Gray female (lowest bird), pied fawn female
(center bird), gray male.

This is one type of nest basket that you can provide for your zebra finches.

books you might be judged a felon.

If your pet escapes you should write it off. The chances of recovery don't justify chasing it down. If your problem is simply inside your aviary or large cage, the first approach should be at night. With patience you may be able to pick up in your hand the bird you want—without a net.

If you must net a bird, buy a net from a dealer who

specializes in them. The fabric should be closely woven to avoid entanglements—a ¼-inch mesh or as fine as 1/16-inch would be a good approximation. The size and shape of the hoop will depend on your aviary. One foot square or one foot in diameter is about as small as most people can use effectively. The larger the hoop, the easier the catch, but as the hoop gets larger, it gets unwieldy and perches get in the way.

The hoop might well be wrapped with a soft fabric so that if your bird collides with or is caught under the hoop, it will not suffer broken bones.

If you have your "druthers," you would be well advised to make your captures at night, by hand.

FINCHES AT NIGHT

Your zebra finches are diurnal. They sleep at night and are active during the light hours. Actually they will begin to roost for the night about an hour before dusk. The young are fed intermittently during the day only, and it is your job to give them the peace and quiet they are accustomed to at night.

This is especially important for breeders because if a setting adult is kicked off the eggs at night and it is really dark, it may

not find its way back and the eggs or fledglings will take a chill—perhaps fatally.

So plan your day around the natural habits of the birds and get the chores done completely at least one hour before dusk. A dim light in or close to the aviary at night may be of value if the birds are scary. A ten watt lamp in a hundred-square-foot room is more than ample and seven and one-half watts will probably suffice. Ten watts for one hundred hours is one kilowatt hour—and that costs less than ten cents. If you have your birds in a large cage or aviary, the lamp might well be mounted under a large "pie pan" reflector and it will then also provide warmth for sick or weak birds. Watch it at night—it may help you spot a health problem.

QUARANTINING NEW BIRDS

If you are interested in adding birds from another aviary, do it only if you are absolutely sure of the health conditions at the source. If in doubt, isolate the newcomers for at least two weeks, preferably in another building, at least in another room. Don't be the carrier of disease as you go from newly introduced birds to your own valued stock.

Above:_Chestnut-flanked white pair; a pair of fawns._ **Facing page:**
Maintaining purity of ground color and strength of markings is a problem with the chestnut-flank mutation.

Left: *Most mutations in zebra finches have resulted in a dilution of the normal colors, as this bird—a silver—shows.* **Below:** *Whether you purchase just zebras, or other finches like this masked grass finch (Poephila personata), remember to always quarantine new birds.*

Illness

Start with healthy birds from a reliable source. Keep them dry and out of drafts. Feed them good millet and supplement the millet with other grains, green vegetables, minerals, grit, clean water. Don't introduce sick birds or even birds which haven't been in a quarantine of some sort. Let them sleep all night every night without interuption, no noisy mice, no flashing lights. Give them sufficient room.

All right, you did all that. Now enjoy your birds; chances are good they will never have a sick day. But what if . . .? you with the hardy zebras ask.

First, go over the checklist of food, water, shelter—the basics. Then evaluate the damage. Did you simply lose one bird because it flew into a window and broke its neck or is there an epidemic

Above: *silver male, with inset showing cheek-patch variation.* **Below:** *cream male.*

Above: silver female. Below:cream female.

in your aviary? Look for signs. Ruffled feathers, eyes that appear small, much daytime sleeping, little eating, wet vents, running nostrils, no chirping.

You will have to be a detective because most bird diseases are hard to diagnose positively without an autopsy.

There are several courses of action after you have gone over the obvious things first. See a veterinarian and be prepared to pay for the visit. He may have to work as hard on your bird as he does on Fifi, the three hundred dollar poodle.

Second, study the diseases of birds in a specialized book. There are several. Stroud's book on canary diseases is applicable to zebra finches as well. Margaret L. Petrak edited a comprehensive treatise on *Diseases of Cage and Aviary Birds;* it is excellent.

Another excellent textbook is *Bird Diseases* by Arnall and Keymer. This is a 528 page classic, profusely illustrated in color.

Third, apply several general therapies which have saved many birds in the past. Work fast. Bird diseases frequently gallop. Raise the temperature to 85-90°F. and hold it until there is recovery. Then lower it *gradually* over several days to the normal cage or aviary temperature. Add a broad base antibiotic such as Aureomycin or tetracycline to the drinking water. These drugs are great to cure disease, but if you use them constantly they will destroy all the normal bacteria in the bird's digestive system; the bird will be cured of disease but will starve to death even if fed heavily because, without the bacteria, no bird will digest its food.

Offer food treats, keep the cage clean, don't interrupt sleep, remove infected birds or otherwise segregate healthy birds from unhealthy ones, if possible. The Petrak book previously mentioned measures 8 x 11 inches and has 528 pages, so you have a real task if the general remedies don't work.

PARASITES
Birds are also bothered by other cage companions you should eliminate. These are the many species of jointed-leg creatures. Here we consider the animals in the tremendous phylum Arthropoda including the class Insecta and the class Arachnida. The insects include mosquitoes, flies and lice. The arachnids include mites, ticks and spiders.

In both classes some are scavengers and some are parasites. "Some" is the wrong word—there are hundreds of species, some known, some unknown, some large enough to swat, others so small you need a microscope merely to see them and a high-power microscope to

The red mite is one of several parasites that can trouble your bird. Treatment of pests such as these is usually most effective when done in two stages. You must kill the parasites on the bird as well as those in the cage. Signs that your pet is infested include frequent scratching and restlessness at night, and of course the actual sight of the parasite on your bird or in the cage.

examine them. Don't bother; it will get you nowhere.

Bird lice are a bother which you will control, but many species of mites and all ticks are genuine enemies which you must actively fight. Fortunately the life style of the parasitic mite helps you win the battle against it. It is a nocturnal feeder. During the night, the mite sucks blood and during the day it hides and deposits eggs—in crevices and cracks of the cage or aviary.

So, during the daylight hours your birds are rid of the mites and you should take advantage of this fact. Place a white cotton rag over a cage of birds in the evening before you retire. Examine it the following morning after your breakfast. Mites will have crawled off the birds and settled in the folds of the cloth. Good. Fold up the cloth and burn it. Then, that same morning put your mite-infested birds into a cage which you recently sterilized with washing soda and boiling water and then you should sterilize the cage they had been in. Get into all the hiding places in the aviary with gamma benzene hexachloride. Do this once every ten days for three or four cycles, and you will have wiped out most or all the mites. Then do it once every

Above: *two views of a crested gray male.* **Facing page, top:** *a crested fawn penguin female.* **Right:** *a young crested gray female.* **Facing page, bottom:** *back and front views of the rare black-breast mutation.*

other month or sooner if the mites show up again.

Ticks need the mechanical picking or chemical treatments mentioned below and lice, mosquitoes, flies will succumb to pyrethrum compounds, paradichlorobenzene or a no-pest strip used intermittently. Remember that a light spray or dusting of pyrethrum is safe for all birds including finches, but too much exposure to a no-pest strip or to gamma benzene hexachloride might possibly be dangerous for some of the more delicate species of birds. If convenient, move the birds out while any high-power insecticide is working.

Paradichlorobenzene, the famous clothes-moth control, is effective against lice and mice. Put some crystals near a louse-infested cage for a few days now and then, and if the treatment proves effective, continue it.

Some bird keepers report that they control some arthropod pests with a spray they mix. It contains one part of Listerine and four parts of Witch Hazel, but there is not now and probably never will be one certain cut-and-dried sure control for these pests and parasites.

Don't waste your time trying to identify lice, fleas, ticks, and mites. One reliable source of information about them states that of the million known species of arthropods, there are more than twenty-five hundred species of lice which are associated with birds. Additionally, there are fifteen hundred species of fleas, many of which parasitize birds. There are more than fifteen thousand species of ticks and mites, of which there are hundreds found only on birds. Frequently the host-parasite relationships are complicated. One bird may have several lice, flea and mite species on or in its skin, feathers, nasal passages or leg scales. Some of these arthropods eat other arthropods and some limit their activity to feces or wastes which accumulate in the nest. A cage or aviary bird wholly rid of all these pests would be unusual, to say the least. Of course you should aim to eliminate them, but nevertheless be satisfied even if you merely succeed in controlling them.

Several government agencies concerned with our personal or environmental health have established rules and guidelines for manufacturers of insect control chemicals. These rules lead to tests which should assure than an insecticide is not dangerous to any but a particular organism. Unfortunately, these tests are time-consuming and expensive. Many proven lice, mite and tick remedies of the past are no longer in the marketplace. Worse, there are not apt to be any substitutes for them in the foreseeable future because the cost of proving their safety would wipe out any possible profit. The old books (and this one does too) mention preparations which may be banned by the time you read these words. Join a fanciers' association, subscribe to a magazine, talk to your pet shop proprietor. These are the only ways you will be able to keep current with the insecticide business.

BONES

Once in a great while a caged finch will break a leg or a wing. Many bird keepers have kept hundreds of finches for decades and never had it happen, but it might.

If this is as a result of frail bones because of a calcium deficiency, you should look to minerals and vitamin D. If the problem is in the cage design, the answer will be obvious. To the extent that long toenails may prevent a bird from properly perching on its perch, resulting in a fall which could cause a broken wing or leg, then the toenails need a clipping.

What to do with the injured bird? You decide, but here are a few hints and guidelines. Splints, consisting of a ¼ inch by 3/8 inch piece of transparent household mending tape have been used with success by some

This female brown wing is one example of the many color variations that occur in zebra finches.

fanciers. A hospital cage with no perches, quiet isolation, warmth and rest sometimes suffices for spontaneous mending of the broken bone. Amputation is sometimes necessary. One-legged birds will thrive for their normal lifespan, but they will not breed since both legs are needed for a bird to keep its balance during copulation.

Top:*a fawn male(left), a juvenile black-breasted male.* **Below:***black-breasted male; note lack of barring on uppertail coverts in this bird.*

Top: *a white male; note flecking on back, a show fault that sometimes disappears in subsequent molts.* **Below:** *a black-breasted female.*

Wings are even less frequently broken and they generally mend within three weeks of quiet isolation in a hospital cage. There is not much you can do about a broken wing on a finch, but if you wish to go to the expense, you might consult your veterinarian.

CLAWS

The normal length of the four claws ("nails") on each foot is perhaps 1/16 or 1/8 inch longer than the part with a blood supply in it. If the nails grow corkscrewed or overly long, perching and even hopping will become difficult. Should such a long-nailed bird attempt to incubate a clutch of eggs, it will surely puncture a few.

Clip the nails or finches with a fingernail clipper or small sharp scissors. You will be able to see the blood vessels when you look through the nails toward the light. Clip 1/16 inch beyond the end of this pink portion. If you inadvertently draw blood, and really this is unnecessary, touch the claw end with a styptic pencil or a little alum powder and the slight bleeding will immediately stop.

Many birds go through their years of life with no nail clipping, so don't do it routinely, but rather on an infrequent as-needed basis.

FEATHER PLUCKING

You will not confuse natural normal molting with feather plucking. The molt is usually a seasonal summertime thing. The molting bird does not end up with bald spots; it just looks a bit ragged for several weeks.

Feather plucking is a vice. Some birds do it to other birds. Isolate the offender and the victim or victims will recover in a month or two. Some birds do it to themselves. Frequently the cause is overcrowding or lack of minerals, especially salt in the diet. These are things you can correct.

Sometimes mites are the irritant and the bird tears out its own feathers as it scratches sore spots. Your pet supply store probably handles anti-plucking sprays which may be applied to the victim. These are frequently effective but you would be well advised to search out the cause and correct it, rather than to go only after the symptom.

If you have a pair with an aggressive male and an uncooperative female, you may be witnessing some pre-nuptial funny business. This generally shows up as a loss of feathers on the back of the neck of the female. She will probably recover completely and go on to raise a big healthy family.

Index

Activity, 20
Adaptation to habitats, 17
Aging, 44
Aviaries, 24
Bathing, 20, 58–61
Breeding, 8, 72–73
Broken bones, 89
Cage furnishings, 65–68
Cage selection, 64
Cage space, 29, 64
Chestnut-eared finch, 13
Cholesterol, 56
Claw clipping, 92
Clutch size, 43–44
Coloration, 8, 32, 38–41
Communicable disease, 29
Crested zebra finches, 40
Diet, 46
Domesticated zebra finches, 16
Dust bathing, 62
Eating, 20
Eggs, 44
Feather plucking, 92
Food supplements, 51
Grain storage, 52
Green foods, 51
Grit, 57
Grubs, 46
Hardiness, 24
Hazards, 68–72
Hybrids, 40

Illness, signs of, 84
Insects as food, 51
Longevity, 24
Millet, 8, 46
Molting, 21, 92
Mutations, 40
Oiling, 62
Overcrowding, 25–29
Pair bonds, 21
Parasites, 84–89
Pecking order, 24–25
Pesticides, 85–89
Quarantining new birds, 77
Reproduction, 21
Roosting, 20
Seed, 46
Sexing, 44
Sociability, 24, 42–43
Spray millet, 48
Sunbathing, 62
Territories, 20
Vitamins, 57–58
Water, 17, 58–61
Water storage, 52
Wild zebra finches, 16
Young birds, 44
Zebra finch noises, 20
Zebra Finch Society, 8
Zebra Finch Society standards,
    32–38

ZEBRA FINCHES
KW-055